Also in this series

THE CAVES OF DERBYSHIRE

Compiled by
TREVOR D. FORD

with the assistance of
D. ALLSOP and R. J. A. TRAVIS

on behalf of the
Derbyshire Caving Association.

DALESMAN PUBLISHING COMPANY LTD.,
CLAPHAM (Via LANCASTER)
YORKSHIRE
1964

PRINTED IN GREAT BRITAIN BY
ATKINSON AND POLLITT, KENDAL,
WESTMORLAND

Contents

The Maps

Introduction

THIS manual of Derbyshire caves is primarily intended for the use of cavers, to guide them in their explorations and researches. For the experts the compilers hope they have provided an accurate summary of the present state of knowledge. For novices they hope the manual will show what their elders have done and where the gaps in our knowledge lie, so that the new generation can help to fill them in.

The compilers hope that their work is as accurate as possible but fully realise that, not having personal knowledge of some areas, there are bound to be some omissions and errors. We hope that these will be pointed out to us in the interests of an improved edition in years to come.

In the absence of a manual such as this in the past, it has been inevitable that some caves have been discovered independently by different cavers, and have received different names. In view of this we have tried to use the name with priority by age—that is, first name sticks—but in a few cases a more recent name has come into general use and we have accepted this. Sometimes the same name has been applied to more than one cave and we have tried to clarify this.

The compilers have relied heavily on caving literature in places and have tried to give bibliographic references where possible. It is recommended tht when further explorations or researches are attempted on any cave, those concerned should make themselves familiar with the literature of past explorations. Too much duplicated effort has been obvious in the past. There is a national caving lending library in the hands of the Cave Research Group of Great Britain (available to members of C.R.G. or to members of Member Clubs, from E. A. Glennie, Seaton House, Shrublands Road, Berkhamstead, Herts., on payment of return postage). Another library is in the British Speleological Association headquarters at Settle.

Future caving must be fully recorded to be of use to all cavers. Club newsletters serve a useful purpose to that club's members, but the more important data of factual descriptions or accounts of findings should be more widely circulated by means of the national journals, such as *Transactions of the Cave Research Group of Great Britain*, and *Cave Science*. Any record of a cave must be accompanied by an accurate Grid Reference, together with a brief note on its location. A few cave names have had to be left out of this manual as the compilers have little more than a name, with no idea of where or what it is.

Caves with archaeological material need special treatment if all the information is to be obtained. Many deposits were ruined in earlier times by "treasure trove" digging without thought of careful analysis. If you find anything worth investigation, ask the Peakland Archaeological Society for advice, or your local museum.

The preservation of cave formations is something which no caver should need to be reminded of, but all too often a once beautiful gotto has little left but stumps of stalactites, or has the once snow-white stalagmites plastered with mud. Let others appreciate your findings.

Many Derbyshire caves are entered through old lead mines where special precautions may need to be taken. False floors or stacked deads (loose boulders) supported on rotting timbers are all too common and should be avoided. Bad air is extremely rare in caves, and is rare in lead mines, but may occasionally be met where there are rotting timbers, or where levels are driven through shale, where sulphuretted hydrogen and methane may occur with carbon dioxide.

The compilers would like to acknowledge the help they have received from B. Chandler, J. Randles, G. H. Workman, M. E. Smith, M. Luff, P. Winter, and many others.

The Derbyshire Caving Association

THE Association was formed in 1960 to provide a link in their activities between the 30 or so independent caving clubs operating in Derbyshire, in order to prevent overlap of investigations, to co-ordinate meets programmes so that two or more clubs did not arrive at one cave at the same time and, most important, to provide a negotiating body in cases of access difficulties. At the time of writing the Association is supported by almost all the larger clubs and by some of the smaller, but there is still much to be desired. In view of increasing access problems only a united organisation, dealing with the responsible authorities can hope to get definite access arrangements. The Cave Research Group can look after this on a national level, but in Derbyshire, only the Association, by means of personal approach, can deal with some matters.

The chairman is D. Allsop, of 5 Bath Road, Buxton; and the secretary, G. H. Workman, "Stonebrack," Peak Forest, via Buxton.

Access to Caves

The listing of a cave in this manual is no proof of the existence of a right-of-way to the cave. Permission **must** be sought from the owner. Failure to do this may result in access being denied to all cavers.

Observe the Country Code at all times. Close all gates behind you. Do not leave litter. Behave in a quiet and orderly manner.

Classification

The entries in this manual are classified in the usual way.

E.C.	Easy Cave
M.C.	Moderate Cave
D.C.	Difficult Cave
V.D.C.	Very Difficult Cave
S.C.	Severe Cave
S.S.C.	Super Severe Cave
E.P.	Easy Pothole
M.P.	Moderate Pothole
D.P.	Difficult Pothole
V.D.P.	Very Difficult Pothole.
S.P.	Severe Pothole
S.S.P.	Super Severe Pothole
Dig	Being dug at present or dug in the past and abandoned
Arch.	Of archaeological importance
Show	Commercialised for Tourists
S	After a bibliographic reference indicates that it includes a Survey Plan.

The compilers cannot accept responsibility for the classification, or any other parts of the entries, although every effort has been made to check.

Conservation

A number of caves in Derbyshire have been scheduled as Sites of Special Scientific Importance by the Nature Conservancy and others are under consideration. While this does not give any right of access it does provide legal protection against destruction by quarrying, tipping rubbish, etc. If any such cave is found to be threatened the facts should be reported at once to the Nature Conservancy, 19 Belgrave Square, London, S.W.1, and to the Cave Research Group (Hon. Asst. Sec., Dr. G. T. Warwick, Geography Dept., University, Birmingham).

The following are scheduled sites :—

Giant's Hole, Eldon Hole, Nettle Pot, Peak Cavern, Treak Cliff Cavern, Plunge-Hole-Poole's Cavern-Wye Head System, Creswell Crags and Caves.

Also the following areas, including their caves :—Manifold Valley, Dovedale, Winnants and Mam Tor and Windy Knoll, Chrome and Parkhouse Hills, Hob's House, Cressbrookdale, Bradwell Dale and Lathkill Dale.

Caving Safety Code

1. NEVER descend on a single rope.

2. NEVER climb anything without the use of a LIFELINE and keep the man holding the lifeline belayed.

3. NEVER try to swim fully clothed or you will almost certainly be dragged down unless on a lifeline.

4. NEVER descend a cave liable to sudden flooding if the weather is unsettled.

5. NEVER have more than one man on an ascent or descent at a time.

6. NEVER carry equipment up or down a pitch; haul it on a rope.

7. NEVER climb elektron ladder with boots fastened by the hook method as they catch on the ladder sides and are very difficult to free on a swinging ladder.

8. NEVER take alcohol before or during a descent.

9. DO check all your equipment regularly.

10. DO wherever possible find out all you can about a cave before you go down. Most caving clubs will give you a plan if you write and ask.

11. DO take spare food with you underground.

12. DO wear warm clothing, wool next to the skin is best.

13. ALWAYS CARRY SPARE LIGHTING.

14. ALWAYS tell someone where you are going and what time you expect to be back.

15. CAVING is not an endurance test, do not try to force members of the party to go further than they want to go.

16. NEVER GO UNDERGROUND ALONE.

On ANY trip, the leader should ensure that all members of the party are fit, for the trip concerned, and that they have adequate clothing, lighting, and a supply of food. Exposure can affect persons very rapidly underground, and if one member of a team starts to tire, the leader should see that he has immediate assistance and that he gets to the surface at the earliest moment, even if it means abandoning the trip.

It is useful to carry a whistle down potholes and to learn the whistle code. 1 blast—STOP. 2—UP. 3—DOWN.

If you want to go caving join a good caving club and learn the correct way to climb rope and elektron ladders, the use of knots and rope.

REMEMBER ALSO that the attitude of cavers to farmers in the past few years has made them very bitter towards the caving world in general. Always ask permission to descend any cave or pothole and treat the farmer's land and property with respect.

The Derbyshire Cave Rescue Organisation has under its control fully equipped and competent teams of volunteer rescue workers. These teams consist of groups of expert cavers who, with full rescue equipment, can be at the scene of an accident within a very short time of the alarm being given.

Each caving area of Derbyshire and surrounding district has one or more of these teams allotted to it who know the caves in that area in great detail so that no time is wasted in bringing the injured man to the surface once the alarm has been given.

If you do get into difficulties and a man is injured do not hesitate to send for help, as delay in the cold and wet of a cave could prove fatal to the injured man.

TO BRING HELP

TELEPHONE COUNTY POLICE (MATLOCK 3131) OR ANY DERBYSHIRE POLICE STATION.

ASK FOR CAVE RESCUE.

GIVE FULL DETAILS OF THE CAVE : NAME AND DISTRICT, Etc.

YOUR OWN NAME.

WHERE YOUR ARE TELEPHONING FROM.

WHAT INJURIES THE MAN HAS.

STAY AT THE TELEPHONE AND AWAIT THE ARRIVAL OF THE POLICE SO THAT YOU CAN ACT AS A GUIDE TO THE CAVE.

In the Case of an Accident

1. Injured person should be kept warm, moved out of air currents or water. Remember shock and exposure are likely to be far more dangerous than moving him.
   Administer what ever first aid is desirable or possible. Give hot sweet tea if possible.
   DO NOT GIVE ALCOHOL.

2. DO NOT LEAVE THE INJURED PARTY ALONE. Send a competent person to fetch help. Ensure that he has an accurate picture of the situation; the requirements of the party, the condition of the injured and the extent of his injuries. He must

9

go to the nearest telephone and phone the police, remain at the telephone, give them full details, the phone number, and await any further instructions.

3. If possible try to start to move the casualty out before the rescue party arrives.

BUT IF THERE IS ANY SUSPICION OF A BACK INJURY DO NOT ATTEMPT TO MOVE THE VICTIM OR PERMA-NENT INJURY COULD RESULT.

**The police will at all times call out the
Derbyshire Cave Rescue.**

THE cave rescue organisation cannot stress too much the need for very great care to be taken underground where even the slightest accident could prove to be very serious in a deep cave or pothole.

———

**STICK AT ALL TIMES TO
THE CAVING SAFETY CODE.**

THE CAVES

ALDERY CLIFF CAVES   Digs

> 088667 to 093664

See Map No. 5

Earlsterndale.

Altitude 1,000ft.

On west slopes of Aldrey Cliff, ½ mile south-west of village.   One small
  cave above Underhill Farm; two badger lairs ½ mile to S.E. and
  fissure pot on crest above.   One of the badger lairs has been dug
  out for 30 feet.

References : P. Tottle 1959.   The Lyre, Vol. 1, No. 3, p. 60.

ALPORT TUFA CAVES   E.C.

> 221646

Alport-by-Youlgreave.

Altitude 450ft.   Length 20ft.

A unique series of small rock-shelter type caves in late Pleistocene
  tufa.   Situated immediately north of road.   Variously used as
  hen-houses and cart-park, but potentially of archaeological interest.
  One cave partly collapsed after 1963 frosts exposing moon-milk
  in cavities in tufa.

ALPORT QUARRY FISSURE   Lost

Near Youlgreave.

A fissure which yielded red deer remains, according to Bemrose
  (Victoria County History, p. 36).

ANGELINA'S CAVERN (Matlock Bath)

Old name for Speedwell Cavern, Matlock Bath.

ASHOVER SWALLETS   Digs ?

> 352632

Ashover.

Three choked swallets (locally called Dumbles) near Black Swan Inn.
  Known as Spout Swallow Hole, Bull Hole, and Tunnel Hole.

ASH TREE CAVE Arch.

515376

Whitwell.

Neolithic burial in small cave.
References : Armstrong, A.L., 1951-7; Derbys. Arch. Journal, Vols.
LXX—LXXVI.

ASHWOOD DALE CAVE E.C.

069730

Ashwood Dale, Buxton.

Altitude 1,000ft. Length 20ft.

On north side of dale, immediately east of sewage works. Go up
path under bridge and cave is high up on right. 15 feet passage,
squeeze past boulder into small chamber. Might repay archaeological digging as it is probably the cave which yielded a few
Romano-British remains to Salt in 1895.

References : Turner (and Salt) Ancient Remains near Buxton, p. 75;
F. Haverfield 1905 in Victoria County History, p. 238; Eldon
Pothole Club Newsletter, Vol. 4, No. 1. Vol. 5, No. 10. S.

ASHWOOD DALE RESURGENCE

090722

Near Buxton.

Altitude 820ft.

A large volume of water rises from an impenetrable crack to left of
pumphouse, south side of road. It is used for water supply.
Source unknown.

Reference: Eldon Pothole Club Newsletter, Vol. 5, No. 10.

AXE EDGE SWALLET HOLES

See Map No. 4

Buxton.

Altitude 1,400ft.

A number of promising swallow holes and small caves. See separate
entries under Axe Hole, Jakes Hole, Nail Pot, Plunge Hole, Stanley Moor Cave, Turncliff Hole.

These and several other sinks along the limestone boundary could
be promising digs.

AXE HOLE

044713

Stanley Moor, Buxton.

Altitude 1,250ft. Length 200ft.

In first shakehole north of Stanley Moor Reservoir. Squeeze down
for 12 feet, tight rift 8 feet. Further sideways squeeze for 10
feet. Left turn into walking passage for 20 feet, terminating in
muddy sump. Crawl beyond in muddy 3 feet high passage round
several bends and undulating to final chamber. Climbing into
roof leads to small chambers with straw stalactites. Turning
right at entrance rift it is possible to squeeze into sandy crawl for
60 feet.

Tackle : Rope useful at entrance and down rift. 50ft.

BADGER HOLE

Stoney Middleton.   See Bossen Hole.

BAGSHAW CAVERN

172809

Bradwell.

Altitude 788ft. O.D. Length 10,000ft.

Formerly known as Mulespinner Mine.

On southern outskirts of Bradwell village. Found in 1806 by lead
miners. Entrance covered by small stone building. Descend
steps in vein then turn left along obvious passage to the Dungeon,
a large pothole in the floor which can be descended by single
rope for 18 feet (ladder advisable for novices) to reach lower
levels trending eastwards for a third of a mile, with pools, crawls
and grottos, ending close to resurgence in Bradwell Dale. For
Upper levels continue beyond Dungeon westwards to the Hippodrome, a wide chamber strewn with fallen blocks. Turning left
at Hippodrome a sloping muddy passage leads down to the stream
passage, choked with boulders to left (downstream), and with a
crawl in water upstream eventually leading to a sump. There
are slim possibilities that this could be lowered by digging in dry
weather. Divers found the passage on too tight. Also from
Hippodrome is flat out crawl becoming too tight (the Snake's
pyjamas) and rift passage leading to muddy pot—the Glory
Hole. Halfway from Dungeon to Hippodrome small gated passage on right leads via wet crawls to fine series of grottos and
arduous passages beyond, not fully explored, entrance crawl to
this series very liable to flooding. The grottos come close to

Crystallised Cavern in old show cave just above Dungeon. Tight bedding crawl near here by-passes Dungeon pitch into lower Series.

Tackle : 18ft. ladder and lifeline for Dungeon; 30ft. ladder and 20ft. belay and 50ft. lifeline for Glory Hole.

Permission required from Proprietor, Mr. Revell, Main Road, Bradwell.

References : E. A. Baker c. 1910 " Moors, Crags and Caves of the High Peak," Chapter XXV. **S.**

BALL EYE MINE

286575   See Map No. 8

Cromford.

Altitude 600ft.

On north side of Via Gellia, a series of ramifying mine workings and natural caverns, intermittently worked for lead and fluorspar. Highest level is Rugs Hall, believed to be chamber in which a fossil elephant was found. Some of lower entrances gated. No survey known. Silver formerly extracted from galena.

References: Buckland 1823, Reliquae Diluvianae; Dawkins 1874, Cave Hunting, pp. 284-5; Heath 1882, Derbyshire Archaeological Journal, Vol. IV, p. 162.

BAMFORTH HOLE   D.C.

223757   See Map No. 9

Middleton Dale.

Altitude 700ft. Length 180ft.

Also known incorrectly as Giants Cave.

This name was applied by Pilkington in 1789 but it is unknown which hole he was referring to, and in recent times the name has been applied to several holes (including Carlswark Cavern). The most likely is a rift entrance 12 feet high and 2½ feet wide 60 feet above and 180 feet north-east of Carlswark. This leads via a tight passage into a partly mined chamber, a rubble cone from a hole in the roof, a blocked passage, and a tight crawl leads to a final chamber with two stalagmite bosses.

References : J. Pilkington, 1789, " A View of the Present State of Derbyshire," Vol. 1, p. 78; N. Kirkham 1948, in British Caver, Vol. 21, p. 26.

BANK END QUARRY FISSURE

About 092502

Waterhouses, Staffs.

Now quarried away.

References : E. Brown 1865, Trans. Midland Scientific Association, pp. 34-38.

BATHAM POT   M.P.

152808   See Map No. 2

Bradwell Moor.

Altitude 1,250ft.

Also known as Pigeon Hole, and as Moss Pot. A large open pot, 100 feet long and 50 feet deep. Easy scramble down east end. Old mine workings to west and abortive dig in floor.

700 feet east-north-east is mine shaft 30 feet deep (ladder required) leading into large natural cavern 60 feet high and 40 feet wide (153808).

Some 100 feet further east-north-east is a group of shafts and natural pots some 30 feet deep (ladder required) (154810).

References : P. Tottle 1957; in " The Lyre," Vol. 1, No. 2, pp. 38-41. **S.**

BAT HOUSE CAVE   Arch. E.C.

335523

Near Ambergate.

Altitude 550ft.

A gritstone fissure cave in Shining Cliff Woods, near Alderwasley. Yielded a Roman brooch and pottery.

References : F. Haverfield 1905, Victoria County History of Derbyshire, p. 236; J. Ward 1899, Reliquary, Vol V. **S.**

BEE LOW POT   M.P.

092793

Doveholes.

Situated near group of boulders behind Bee Low Quarry. A heavily fluted shaft ends in a tight fissure.

Tackle required : Ladder and lifeline 25ft.

BEESTON TOR CAVES   E.C.

1054   See Map No. 7

Manifold Valley.

A group of unnamed caves except for St. Bertram's, on Beeston Tor.
Ropes required to descend some.

References : G. H. Wilson 1926, "Some crags and caves of Peakland," pp. 38-47; G. H. Wilson 1934, "Cave hunting holidays in
Peakland," pp. 47-56.

THE BELFRY   M.P.

072866

Kinderscout, Edale.

Altitude 1,800ft. Depth 40ft.
On south edge of Kinderlow End, just below the edge. A maze
caused by the splitting off of gritstone blocks.

BINCLIFFE HOLE   D.C.

114538   See Map No. 7

Manifold Valley.

Altitude 900ft. Length 25ft.

In topmost outcrop above Bincliffe Mine levels. A badger lair. Flat
crawling as far as possible.

BINCLIFFE MINE (The levels)   M.C.

112537   See Map No. 7

Manifold Valley.

Altitude 800ft. Length 1,000ft.

On scrub-covered east side of valley, ½ mile below Beeston Tor.
Several entrances and shafts between 525ft. and 800ft. altitude.
Main level is part mine and part cave and particular care is
needed in exploration. Contains good cave pearls which should
be preserved. No survey known.

BLACK HOLE SWALLET   Dig ?

204772   See Map No. 9

Eyam.

Altitude 1,000ft.

A sink which occasionally takes water 100 yards South-west of Black
Hole Mine. Needs digging.

BLACKWELL DALE CAVE   E.C.

133728

Millers Dale.

Altitude 975ft. Length 200ft.

Opens from east side of main Millers Dale to Taddington road, in
Blackwell Dale. Stooping for first 25 feet then opens into
chamber 20 feet high. After further 60 feet develops into bedding plane which ends in a choke. Reasonable prospects for
digging. Long low crawl on right near entrance leads back to
dale side:

Reference : D. Turner, Stoke-on-Trent, Pothole Club Journal, Vol.
I, No. 1, p. 13.

BLUE JOHN CAVERNS   Show

132832   See Map No. 1

Castleton.

Altitude 1,250ft. Depth about 300ft.

A mile west of Castleton on Mam Tor road. Artificial entrance for
18 feet, then descent of steps to Ladies Walk, sloping passage to
90 feet high Crystallised Cavern. Second stairway leads to Stalactite Cavern and Lord Mulgrave's Dining Room, 140 feet high
and 30 feet wide, where water is first met in a fissure. Several
passages lead off, one to Fairy Grotto and Stemple Cavern, also
reached from Stalactite Cavern. Forward show route ends in
Variegated Cavern, over 100 feet high and 30 feet wide, seen
from ledge 20 feet up. Large passage continues beyond with rock
barrier passable by muddy Rabbit Burrow into final chamber.
Descend to final sump requires 30 feet ladder. Branch passage
leads up to choke with hole at side where one can communicate
with Fairy Grotto.

References : Barnes and Holroyd 1896, Trans. Manchester Geol. Soc.,
Vol. XXIV; Martel (translated by Winder) 1910, The Caverns of
Castleton, S; F. Winder, "An Unconventional Guide to the Caves
of Castleton," S; J. Royse, "Ancient Castleton Caves," S;
T. D. Ford 1955, Proc. Yorks. Geol. Soc., Vol. 30, S.

BOAT HOUSE CAVE   Arch.

534740

Creswell.

On south side of gorge at east end. A low arch.

Reference : A. L. Armstrong 1936, Derbys. Archeo. Journal, Vol. 57,
page 129.

BODENS QUARRY CAVE
2958

Matlock.

A bone cave intersected by quarrying "in a declivity about 20 feet above the river Derwent on the east side of the Heights of Abraham." Finds include bones of rhinoceros, hyaena, bear and bison. Exact site no longer known.

Reference: R. Law 1878, Trans. Manchester Geol. Soc., Vol. 15, pp. 52-55.

BONDOG HOLE
Middleton-by-Wirksworth.

Listed by Farey (1811, p. 293) "in 4th lime—stalactites." Location now unknown.

BOREHOLE SWALLET   Dig
049715   See Map No. 4

Stanley Moor, Buxton.

Altitude 1,160ft.

50 yards upstream from Borehole pump house, stream sinks under a wall. Water dye-tested to reappear at Wye Head. Dug out (assisted by collapse!) to 15 feet to uncover tight passage blocked after a few feet. Digging in progress.

Reference: Eldon Pothole Club Newsletter, Vol. 5 and 7.

BOSSEN HOLE   M.C.
224757   See Map No. 9

Stoney Middleton.

Altitude 700ft. Length 100ft.

Also known as Badger Hole or Tacko Hole or Windy Hole. Situated on north side of Middleton Dale. Footpath leads to exposed ledge in centre of limestone cliff. After walking a few feet, rest of cave is crawl, right through buttress of cliff, with short inward branch. Too draughty for naked lights at times. Care needed on ledge.

BOSSEN HOLE
100652

Crowdecote

Altitude 800ft. Length 200ft.

Dry crawl below Orpheus C.C. cottage. Liable to flooding.

BOULDER POT

See Map No. 3

D.P.

164665

Monyash.

Altitude 875ft. Depth 110ft. Length 120ft.

On left of track to Ricklow Quarry from Bakewell-Monyash road among large boulders. Narrow entrance leads to small bone chamber and further descent to crawls. Very tight fissure allows slim cavers to reach bottom of pot. Entrance "corked" with boulders for safety—don't get shut in ! Whole place is unstable—take care !

BRADWELL CAVE

E.C.

See Map No. 2

174806

Bradwell.

Altitude 630ft. Length 60ft.

First cave on left in Bradwell Dale from village. Several short crawls.

BRADWELL DALE CAVE

E.C.

See Map No. 2

173805

Bradwell.

Altitude 600ft. Length 110ft.

Also known as Walker's Grotto.

Second cave on left from village. Obvious entrance leads to single large chamber with stalactite formations now vandalised. Floor muddy and floods in wet weather via small hole on left.

BRADWELL PARISH CAVE

E.C.

See Map No. 2

172805

Bradwell.

Altitude 600ft. Length 65ft.

Also known as Old Brook Cave.

Directly opposite Bradwell Dale Cave. Obvious entrance leads to muddy crawl which has to be reversed feet first. In heavy flood conditions water comes out and is said to come from the stream in Bagshaw Cavern. This has yet to be tested.

Reference : D. Turner 1950, in British Caver, Vol. 21, pp. 22.

BROOK BOTTOM RESURGENCE

056713 See Map No. 4

Near Buxton.

Altitude 1,100ft.

Large wet weather resurgence as "fountains" from 18-inch diameter hole in brook bed, probably fed from water dammed up behind quarry debris ¼ mile up the valley.

BULL PIT E.P.

107815 See Map No. 1

Perryfoot, Castleton.

Altitude 1,180ft.   Depth 80ft.

600 yards east of Perryfoot and north of road.   A large deep open pot-hole choked at bottom with large boulders.   Easy scramble down south-east side.   Various digs in bottom.   Shaft No. 1 is 20 feet deep, then 30 feet crawl in side passage to chamber.   Downward passage and 20 feet pitch leads to second chamber.   Passage over leads to T junction and left is over jagged rocks to third chamber containing a stream.   Other passage leads back to entrance pitch through natural and mined passages.   Digging now abandoned and shaft hidden.

BULL TOR CAVE (Cressbrook)

Alternative name for Ravenscliffe Cave.

Also applied to small cave entrance in same crag about 6 feet wide into long crawl with badger lair.   (174731).

Once known as Good Friday Cave.

CALESDALE CAVE (Lower) M.C.

174653 See Map No. 3

Lathkill Dale.

Altitude 650ft.   Length 320ft.

Near the path up the west side of Calesdale, hidden by undergrowth. Two low entrances below path join inside in stream passage. Low crawl for 100 feet leads to No. 1 Chamber, 20 feet wide, 30 feet long and 10 feet high.   On the right the floor rises to Stalactite Chamber with avens above.   Across No. 1 Chamber the passage continues for 200 feet in low crawls with small chambers.   Final chamber has several avens and small holes leading down to water.

During 1959 drought terminal stream passage was dry and was forced for 60 feet to a boulder choke. Hammering was said to have been heard in Lathkill Head Cave at the time.

Passages are active in wet weather and whole cave is liable to fill completely.

Reference : P. Coates and F. Wicken 1956, in The Speleologist, Vol. 1, No. 4. **S.**

CALESDALE CAVE (Upper)   M.C.

172654   See Map No. 3

Lathkill Dale.

Altitude 775ft. Length 200ft.

There has been considerable confusion between this cave and One Ash Cave (172651) both of which have been partly excavated last century and both of which are of similar dimensions. The name strictly applies to that almost directly above Lower Calesdale Cave, which is entered from a shelf hidden by undergrowth high on the west side of the dale. Main passage divides after 75 feet into two crawls, that on right has stalactite formations.

Excavated material now in Manchester Museum.

References : R. Pennington 1875, Quar. Journal Geol. Soc., pp. 238-40; J. W. Jackson and W. Storrs Fox 1913, Geol. Mag., pp. 259-262; P. Coates and F. Wicken 1956, The Speleologist No. IV, pp. 174-5.

CALLING LOW HOLES   E.P.

181648   See Map No. 3

Lathkill Dale.

Altitude 1,020ft. Depth 40ft.

Also known as Callenge Low Holes.

East of the head of Calesdale, south of the Farm. A group of fluted shafts up to 40 feet deep (ladder required) becoming tight in solid rock. Some now partly full of rubbish.

References : Farey 1811, p. 293, " deep open holes in 1st lime."

CAN HOLES   Digs ?

041721   See Map No. 4

Burbage, Buxton.

Altitude 1,200ft.

Small sink near Macclesfield- and Leek-Buxton road junction where water can be seen falling between boulders for 5 feet.

Another sink at 040718 takes more water in wet weather.

CARLSWARK CAVERN D.C.

221758 See Map No. 9

Stoney Middleton.

Altitude 600ft. Length about 4,000ft.

Also known once as Charleswark Cavern and as The Wonder Cavern.

Low crawl entrance at foot of cliff midway between Stoney Middleton and the Eyam turning, at road level. Easily recognised by cavers' litter. Inside follow right hand passage for 200 feet to sump with rift above. Climb rift and hole at top leads up into floor of upper series. Left leads shortly to mine workings close to cliff face; right is main passage leading to roof fall in Noughts and Crosses Chamber. Passage branches beyond—left leads to impenetrable crawl. Ahead via a squeeze to chokes. Right via a muddy passage to a further junction. Left leads to chokes at foot of Eyam Dale shaft entrance (30ft. ladder). Right leads down dip to old terminal sump, now opened by B.S.A. to New Series. Tight crawl through old sump leads to Cockle Passage, so-called from fossil shells in roof, squeeze past boulder then leads to 1,400 feet of passages including grottos, traces of mineworkings beneath Eyam Dale, and to the downstream end of the sump in the entrance passage. This has been passed in time of extreme drought. Several choked passages and a sump extend in a north-westerly direction and digging is in progress.

Tackle : 50ft. rope useful in entrance rift with novices. 30ft. ladder and lifeline needed for Eyam Dale Shaft.

The entrance to the new series is to be gated.

References : B. King 1962, Cave Science, Vol. IV, No. 32, pp. 377-383, S; D. P. Jefferson 1961, Bull. Peak District Mines Hist. Soc., Vol. I, No. 4, pp. 37-43.

CARSINGTON PASTURE CAVE E.C.

243541

Brassington.

Altitude 1,000ft. Length 25ft.

Single chamber with walk in entrance in hollow in middle of Pasture. Soot on roof and chimney shaft suggest inhabitation at some time.

CASCADE CAVERN M.P.

158664 See Map No. 3

Monyash.

Altitude 850ft. Length 125ft. Depth 60ft.

Formerly known as Eagle Mine, and locally called Rumbling Hole.

Wide mine shaft 40 feet deep leads to short passage. Further 15 feet pitch (rotten wooden ladder should be avoided) drops into natural passage 100 feet long with two waterfalls. Stream disappears in choked swallet.

Tackle : Entrance shaft 40ft. ladder and lifeline. Second pitch 20ft. handline.

Reference : S. Gee 1957, The Lyre, Vol. I, No. 2.

CASTLE CAVE   E.C.
150513

Dovedale.

Altitude 550ft. Length 15ft.

Inviting large cave entrance at top of scree in crags 200 yards south west of Dovedale stepping stones. Closes completely in 15 feet.

CAULDON LOW CAVERN
0748

Waterhouses, Staffs.

Bone cave now completely quarried away and exact position not known.

References : Trans. North Staffs. Field Club, Vol. XL, p. 85, and Vol. XLI, p. 92.

CAVEDALE CAVES (No. 1)   E.C.
150827   See Map No. 1

Castleton.

Altitude 730ft. Length 20ft.

Immediately on right on entering dale, under overhanging rock. Short mine level with evidence of solutional activity.

No. 2. Altitude 875ft. Length 15ft.
150826

At top of slope under south side of Castle Keep. A bedding cave 8 feet wide and 18 inches high. Crawling on rubbish for 15 feet.

Archaeologically excavated.

References : R. Pennington 1877, Barrows and Bone Caves of Derbyshire, p. 53. R. Pennington 1875, Quar. Jour. Geol. Soc., p. 238.

No. 3. Altitude 850ft. Length 6ft.
150826

Below and to west of last. Halfway down slope, close to old waterpipe. Small rock shelter ending in collapsed boulders. Reputed to have extended further at one time, and to have been dug archaeologically. This may be the Creep Hole, noted by Pennington as connecting with a cave in the top of Peak Cavern Gorge, probably Peveril Castle Cave.

Reference : R. Pennington 1875, Barrows and Bone Caves of Derbyshire, p. 57.

No. 4. Altitude 850ft. Depth 100ft.

149825

In cleft north of footpath up dale, where dale narrows and steepens. Narrow fissure descended by Puttrell into roof of Orchestra Chamber of Peak Cavern. Now blocked with concrete.

No. 5. Altitude 900ft. Length 20ft.

150826

Also known as Peveril Castle Cave.

Some 20 feet higher and to left of 2 and 3 above. Below west wall of Castle Keep in top of Peak Cavern Gorge. Low chamber sloping down to north-east for 20 feet mostly 2½ feet high. Reputed to connect with 3 above.

No. 6. See Gorge Top Cave.

CHELMORTON CAVERN   E.C.

105717

Near Buxton.

Altitude 950ft. Length 20ft.

Large cave entrance immediately east of Churn Holes, in Marl Dale, the southern branch off Deepdale, near Topley Pike.

It is not certain whether this is the cave listed by Farey (1811), p. 293.

CHESHIRE WOOD CAVE   M.C.

114534   See Map No. 7

Manifold Valley.

Altitude 800ft. Length 40ft.

At top of wood in a crag ½ mile below Beeston Tor. A bedding crawl with some formations.

CHRISTMAS CAVE   M.P.

111818   See Map No. 1

Castleton.

Altitude 1,220ft.   Depth 100ft.

In dry valley west of Snelslow, 300 yards south of swallet. A fissure
   cave dug by B.S.A. in 1947. Ends in impenetrable choke.

Reference: Salmon and Boldock 1950, Cave Science, No. 11, p. 122.

CHROME HILL CAVE   E.C.

074673   See Map No. 5

Earlsterndale.

Altitude 1,150ft.   Length 20ft.

On north side of Chrome Hill, visible from Dowell Farm. A small
   cave popular with sheep !

References : P. Smith 1960, The Lyre, Vol. I, No. 3.

CHROME HILL RIFT   D.C.

072674   See Map No. 5

Earlsterndale

Above and to west of Chrome Hill Cave. A sporting traverse down
   into a crawl ending in a dripstone barrier.

Reference : P. Smith 1960, The Lyre, Vol. I, No. 3.

CHURCH HOLE CAVE   Arch.

533741.

Creswell.

Altitude 300ft.   Length 200ft.

In Creswell Crags gorge, $\frac{1}{4}$ mile east of village. Entrance narrow,
   tapering opening. On south side of gorge. Archaeological remains excavated now in British Museum.

References : Armstrong, in reports in Derbyshire Archaeological
   Journal from Vol. 55 onwards. Geological Survey Memoir on N.
   part of Derbyshire Coalfield 1913, pp. 107-8.

CHURN HOLES

M.C.

105718

Near Buxton.

Altitude 880ft.

At head of Marl Dale, southern branch of Deepdale, near Topley Pike. Two pothole entrances drop into passage reached from third crawl entrance. Short passage ends in crawl. Promising dig, but much loose rock.

Reference : W. Turner 1899, Ancient remains near Buxton, p. 78.

COALPITHOLE RAKE

D.P.

1081   See Map No. 1

Perryfoot, Castleton.

Altitude 1,200ft.

A series of lead mine shafts from 200-600 feet deep. Lower levels now flooded, concealing " lost " swallet 100 yards west of No. 1 shaft in Perrydale. Water rises again at Russet Well, Castleton.

Reference : L. Salmon 1963, Cave Science, Vol. V, No. 33, pp. 36-52.

COALPITHOLE POT   See GAUTRIES HILL POT

COCKSHEAD MINE

V.D.P.

107813   See Map No. 1

Perryfoot, Castleton.

Altitude 1,230ft. Depth 165ft.

Through gate on right coming up hill from Perryfoot, second shaft to east and 50 feet from the wall. Belay ladder to joist across hole. Narrow entrance shaft. East from base leads to cavern and passages. Westwards from shaft bottom leads to 30 feet pitch with loose boulders. Small passage leads off, across second shaft to join up in lower levels by 35 feet shaft.

Lower levels flood in wet weather. Water believed to come from swallets to north.

Note : The first shaft from the road also leads into the mine but is unsafe.

Tackle : 1st pitch Ladder 130ft., Lifeline 150ft. 2nd pitch Ladder 35ft., belay to foot of 1st ladder or take a beam down. Lifeline 50ft.

Reference : B. Chandler 1953, British Caver, Vol. 24, pp. 73-75, S (recorded as S.P. Hole).

COLLIERS PERIL CAVE V.D.C.

Coombs Dale, Stoney Middleton.

A low bedding cave entrance high on hillside near foot of Coombs Dake. Very tight crawl leads to rift, with crawls leading off. Good formations.

Also known as FATIGUE POT.

Reference: P. Tottle 1954, The Speleologist, No. III, pp. 85-91, S.

CONIES DALE POT

131808   See Map No. 1

Peak Forest.

Altitude 1,300ft. Depth 50ft.

One of a series of choked fissures on the slopes north of the head of Conies Dale, temporarily blocked. Most of these fissures have been dug at one time or another but abandoned before reaching rock bottom, so that there is still good promise here. Other fissures at 131810 and 130811 open for a few feet only.

Reference: G. Workman 1954, Cave Research Group Newsletter, No. 49/50.

COTTON CAVE E.C.

127589

Beresford Dale.

Altitude 710ft.

In the grounds of Beresford Estate, Hartington. Entrance well hidden. Contains one small chamber. Charles Cotton is said to have hidden there. Three small rock shelters nearby.

COTTON SWALLET M.C.

089502

Waterhouses.

Altitude 690ft. Length 25ft.

In bed of River Hamps, 450 feet below the bridge. Has a solid rock roof and runs south under river and road. Ends in a choke.
Reference: Clark 1910, Trans. N. Staffs. Field Club.

CRESSBROOK CAVES

See under Lumb Hole (=Cressbrook Resurgence Cave); Ravenscliffe Cave; Bull Tor Cave; Old Cressbrook Cave.

CRESWELL CAVES

A series of archaeological caves in the Magnesian Limestone of East Derbyshire.

See under Pinhole Cave; Church Hole Cave, Mother Grundy's Parlour; Boat House Cave.

References : J. M. Mello and W. B. Dawkins, Quar. Jour. Geol. Soc. 1875, 1876, 1877, 1879. A. L. Armstrong 1925, Jour. Royl. Anthrop. Inst., Vol. 55. A. L. Armstrong 1930, Proc. Prehist. Soc., Vol. VI. A. L. Armstrong 1956, in Sheffield and its Region (Brit. Assn.). Geological Survey Memoir on North Part of the Derbyshire Coalfield 1913, pp. 105-112.

CRITCHLOW CAVE   V.D.C.

171660   See Map No. 3

Lathkill Dale.

Altitude 680ft. Length 500ft.

Directly opposite Lathkill Head Cave, by a lone bush. Downward sloping bedding entrance leads in 20 feet to sharp left and right turn with squeeze into Warren Chamber, then via another passage and small chamber to a large bedding cave. The main passage on the right is over 300 feet long and contains some good formations. Silt choke at end still being dug.

Whole system tight and muddy.

Reference : Derbys. Caving Assn. Newsletter No. 8, May, 1963.

CROSSLOW CAVERN   M.P.

204771   See Map No. 9

Eyam.

Altitude 1,000ft. Depth 80ft. Length 300ft.

A lost cavern listed by Farey in 1811 and recently rediscovered by Peak District Mines Historical Society.

Shaft in enclosure in south-west corner of Field No. 281, 200 yards south-west of Black Hole Mine. On Croslow Rake, 60 feet ladder pitch and 20 feet scramble (lifeline 100 feet) into mine workings. Passage west into natural caverns once used as washing floor. Drainage towards Waterfall Swallet.

THE CROWDWELL   Dig

100653   See Map No. 9

Crowdecote.

Altitude 800ft.

Large resurgence in Upper Dove Valley. Water emerges from culverts below rubbish heap.

Reference : P. Smith 1960, The Lyre, Vol. I, No. 3, p. 60.

CUCKLET CHURCH CAVE

E.C.

216764

See Map No. 9

Eyam.

Altitude 800ft.

High up on west side of Cucklet Delph in a prominent crag. Series of through arches used each year for Plague Commemoration Service.

CUMBERLAND CAVERN

Show

292577

See Map No. 8

Matlock Bath.

Altitude 525ft. Length ¼ mile.

Proceed up Wapping Lane or Clifton Road near the Church. Mined level leads to " pipe " vein workings and natural caverns.

CUNNINGDALE SWALLET

Dig ?

073738

Near Buxton.

Altitude 1,000ft.

At head of Cunningdale, just past allotments in middle of waste ground. The sink takes a small stream largely composed of sewage from a pig farm !

DARFAR CRAG SWALLET

M.P.

096558

See Map No. 7

Altitude 620ft. Depth 90ft.

Manifold Valley.

In wood under Darfar Crag on east bank. Entrance 3 feet wide, 15 feet above river.

Rope pitch of 50 feet followed by 30 feet descent to clay bank and down rock passage for 60 feet. Possible to squeeze past boulder into chamber with pool. Liable to flooding.

Tackle : 50ft. rope.

Another cave in the same crag has Pleistocene and Neolithic remains and is being dug by the Rolls Royce Caving Club, Derby.

DEADMAN'S CLOUGH SWALLET

176801   See Map No. 2

Bradwell Dale.

Altitude about 800ft.

Choked swallet ¼ mile east of Hazlebadge Hall, near Old Pig Tor
End Lead Mine. Takes little water now owing to Reservoirs
higher up.

DEEPDALE CAVE   Dig

097713

Near Buxton.

Altitude 975ft. Length 70ft.

The name strictly applies to a bedding crawl opposite (west) Thirst
House Cave (q.v.) but has often been misapplied to the latter.
Above Deepdale Cave is a rift in the wood being dug, and down
dale from Thirst House is " Pool Cave "—a short flooded mine
level which has been pumped dry and soon ends.

Reference : F. Hammond 1956, The Lyre, Vol. I, No. 1, p. 13.

DELPH HOLE   M.C.

217759   See Map No. 9

Eyam.

Altitude 700ft. Length 130ft.

High on east side of Cucklet Delph, below Auton Crofts plateau.
Entrance is 6 feet high mine level.

After 66 feet from entrance take left hand passage as easiest way of
reaching opposite passage. After 25 feet is a chamber 30 feet
long, with a silted passage running back.

Reference : Pill. 1950, Cave Science, No. 13, p. 223.

DEMON'S DALE ROCK SHELTER   Arch.

169704

Ashford-in-the-Water.

Reference : Armstrong 1948, Archaeological Newsletter, p. 5.

DEVONSHIRE CAVERN   V.D.C.

290854   See Map No. 8

Matlock Bath.

Altitude 700ft.   Length about 1,000ft.   Depth 260ft.

On footpath to Bonsall off north end of Upperwood Road.

A former show cave at first going down the dip of the beds with lower levels, crawls to side and mine galleries in upper parts. Extensive roof falls in places, partly blocking lower series.

30ft. ladder required for blind shafts in floor.

Reference : J. Larson 1954, The Speleologist, Vol. I, No. 3, pp. 121-7, S.

DIDO'S CAVE   M.C.

About 296575   See Map No. 8

Matlock Bath.

Altitude 300ft.

Short passage on east side of Derwent by weir at Masson Mill leads to pool chamber.   Rope useful for return.

DIELASMA CAVE (Castleton)   See TREE HOLE

DOG HOLES RESURGENCE

043727   See Map No. 4

Burbage, Buxton.

Altitude 1,000ft.

Large resurgence behind two small cottages at Dog Holes, which could be the water from the Shay Lodge sinks.

DONKEY HOLE   M.C.

098550   See Map No. 7

Manifold Valley.

Altitude 570ft.   Length 50ft.

Also known as Radcliffe Stables, though Wilson (" Caves and Caving," No. 2, p. 61) suggests that these are two separate holes.

Directly below Thor's Cave, some 30 feet above river.   Entrance of rock shelter type.   Several choked passages.   One crawl leads to chamber with water.

DOVE HOLES CAVES

E.C.

142535

See Map No. 6

Dovedale.

Altitude 700ft.

South-east of Hanson Grange opposite Hall Dale. Two large entrances 55 and 30 feet wide and high. Animal remains excavated can be seen in Buxton, Manchester and Natural History Museums.

DOVE HOLES CAVE

E.C.

077782

Dove Holes, Buxton.

Altitude 970ft. Length 10ft.

Discovered in 1962 by Eldon Pothole Club after clearing rubbish from entrance, which is near Recreation Ground behind March-ington's lorry park. Entrance 3 feet wide and 1 foot high leads into 10 feet square chamber. Possible dig.

DOVE HOLES SWALLET

D.C.

075779

Dove Holes, Buxton.

Altitude 950ft. Length 20ft.

Situated opposite Queen's Hotel where small stream sinks. Eldon Pothole Club dig leads via squeeze to short passage, blocked by boulder, though water can be heard falling beyond. Digging in progress. Swallet takes large amount of flood water, so digging should be well repaid, though recent road-widening debris may have blocked access.

Reference : Eldon Pothole Club Newsletter, Vol. 2, No. 12.

DOVEHOLES DALE SWALLOWS

Digs

Doveholes, Buxton

Altitude about 1,100ft.

Three abortive digs in dale floor at 076778, 087773 and 089772.

References : R. V. Frost 1954, The Speleologist, Vol 1, No. 3, p. 95.

Two fissures were encountered during the excavation of the Doveholes railway tunnel to the west. Both are close to the limestone-shale boundary and still give a large quantity of water which is cul-verted under the lines to the north end of the tunnel. It is not known whether the fissures were explored though it is known that one can be climbed for some 20 feet through a waterfall.

DOVE PIT (Dowel Dale, Earlsterndale)

See OWL HOLE

DOWEL RESURGENCE

075675

See Map No. 5

Earlsterndale.

Altitude 950ft.

Main rising for Dowel Area at foot of dale opposite farm. Fissure impenetrable after 6 feet.

Reference : P. Smith 1960, The Lyre, Vol. I, No. 3, p. 67.

DOWEL HALL CAVE

Arch.

075676

See Map No. 5

Earlsterndale.

Altitude 1,025ft. Length 50ft.

An old resurgence cave some 50 yards up the dale from the present rising. Fissure descending inwards and choked at bottom. Neolithic remains excavated.

References : D. Bramwell 1957-9, Peakland Archeological Newsletters. D. Bramwell 1960, The Lyre, Vol. I, No. 3, S. D. Bramwell 1959, Derbys. Arch. Jour., S.

DRAKE MINE CAVERN

Lost

Winster.

Listed by Farey (1811, p. 293). Believed to be near intersection of Shack Vein and Drake Vein, approximately 244608.

DREAM HOLE

E.C.

275530

Wirksworth.

Altitude 800ft. Depth 50ft.

North of Sprink Wood, south-west of Wirksworth. Large open fissure on summit of hill. Partly mined. Scramble down west end, crawl and then climb. Among remains found was almost perfect skeleton of a rhinoceros, now in Oxford University Museum. No modern excavation of deposits attempted.

References : Buckland 1823, Reliquae Diluvianae (with section drawing). Dawkins 1874, Cave Hunting, pp. 284-5.

DUCE HOLE

Dig ?

181777

See Map No. 9

Great Hucklow.

Altitude 1,000ft.

A choked small swallet at Grindlow, near Great Hucklow. Abortive attempts have been made at digging, so far without success.

Water said to go to Bagshaw Cavern.

There is some confusion over the name. Farey (1811) p. 293 listed Duss Pit—an open hole in 1st lime, and on p. 295 he noted Dowse Hole, Grindlow, near Eyam, a deep open hole. It has certainly not been a deep open hole within memory, and Farey may have referred to either Waterfall Swallet or to an open cavity in Dusty Pit Mine, Eyam.

THE DUNGEONS

E.C.

259609

Wensley.

Altitude 750ft. Length 20ft.

Two landslips in the limestone south-west of Wensley have exposed short lengths of bedding and fissure cave. One is a possible dig.

DUNGEON CAVE

Dig ?

105653

Crowdecote.

High on hill east of Crowdecote. Formerly dug by Orpheus C.C.

EAGLE MINE (Monyash)

**See CASCADE
CAVERN**

ECTON HILL CAVES

M.C.

102574

See Map No. 7

Manifold Valley.

Altitude 1,025ft. Length 25ft.

On crag at summit of south-east end of Ecton Hill. Two entrances: one 3 feet high, becoming very tight before short descent to small chamber. The other is to the south in the same crag, longer but only one chamber.

ECTON COPPER MINES

Mines

097584

Manifold Valley.

These old copper mines are well known to cavers for their cave pearls and other formations in the adits extending up to ¾ mile into the hill. Beware flooded shafts in floor.

Salts Level : behind Ecton House leads into Deep Ecton Pipe workings where it is possible to climb down with the aid of ladders to the Deep Ecton levels and winding house, etc., also reached via a half flooded adit below the Cheese Factory.

Dutchman Level : close to largest hillock on hillside. Half flooded and with good cave formations and extensive old stopes.

Fly Mine : above and to south of Dutchman—a short series of pipe workings.

Apes Tor Level : now flooded but connecting Deep Ecton with north end of hill at river level.

Deep Ecton : Adit entrance below old Cheese factory. Up to waist deep in water, leads into old pipe-workings and Engine House. Beware flooded shafts.

Clayton Adit : Adit on road side, up to knee deep in water. Leads to old underground winding and pumping house. Beware flooded shaft in floor. Good cave-pearls in branch levels. Turn right in winding house, and then left across plank over flooded shaft to reach Cascades, which can be climbed with care to chamber at base of shaft to surface.

Reference : N. Kirkham, " Ecton Mines." Special Publication of the Peak District Mines Historical Society.

ELDERBUSH CAVE

Arch.

097548

See Map No. 7

Manifold Valley.

Altitude 900ft. Length 150ft.

In south-west end of Thor's Crag. Entrance chamber completely excavated. Fissure leads to lower series with good formations. Animals and human remains from Pleistocene to Romano-British.

References : D. Bramwell 1947-52, Peakland Archaeological Society Newsletter, Nos. 1-8. D. Bramwell 1950, Trans. Cave Research Group, Vol. I, No. 4.

ELDON HOLE

D.P.

116809

See Map No. 1

Peak Forest.

Altitude 1,412ft. Depth 245ft.

On southern slopes of Eldon Hill and best approached from Peak Forest on cart track. The largest open pot hole in Derbyshire, 110 feet long and 20 feet wide at the surface.

Upper end of hole is most used for descent. Rope assisted scramble for 70 feet ends at an outward sloping ledge. Belay ladder to boulders and pitons. Lifeline operator must be belayed himself. From bottom of shaft, cavern is reached through timbered passage, intermittently blocked by decaying cows and sheep! Wide cavern inside 90 feet high with good formations. Good light required to see them. Climb on left leads to crawl passage—a possible dig. Fissure on right has been dug out for 60 feet but has run in since. First explorations in 1780 by Lloyd (Phil. Trans. Royal Soc., Vol. 61) show lower shaft in floor with stream at bottom, but this has not been seen since.

Main shaft may also be descended by south end, but difficult owing to overhanging ledges, or in good free hanging 200 feet pitch from east side.

Tackle: North End—1st pitch 100ft. handline, plus lifeline. Main pitch 130ft. ladder, 60ft. belay, 150ft. lifeline.
South End—Ladder 180ft., belay 40ft., lifeline 200ft.
East Side—Ladder 200ft., belay 30ft., lifeline 220ft.

References : Lloyd 1780, Phil. Trans. Roy. Soc., Vol. 61, **S.** Simpson 1949, Cave Science, Nos. 7 and 8. F. Atkinson 1949, Cave Science, No. 8, **S.** G. Workman 1953, Speleologist, Vol. 1, Nos. 2 and 3.

ELDON QUARRY CAVE

114814

Near Castleton.

Altitude about 1,350ft.

An enlarged joint type of cave some 50 feet deep intersected by quarrying during the War and since completely removed. It was well decorated with stalactites. There have been recent rumours about blasting smoke appearing in Eldon Hole about ¼ mile to the south-east.

ETCHES CAVE   M.C.

076676

See Map No. 5

Earlsterndale.

Altitude 1,025ft.   Length 60ft.

100 yards west-north-west of Dowel Resurgence and 75 feet above it. Short rift cave in old quarry dug out by Orpheus C.C. Still being dug.

Reference : P. Smith 1960, The Lyre, Vol. I, No. 3, **S.**

FATIGUE POT (Stoney Middleton)
See COLLIER'S PERIL CAVE

FERN CAVE
298588

Show

See Map No. 8

Matlock.

Altitude 600ft. Length 600ft.

On summit of High Tor, Matlock, connecting with Roman Cave. Very old open worked out lead vein.

FISSURE CAVE (Manifold Valley)
See THOR'S FISSURE CAVE

FLUORSPAR CAVERN
291581

Mine

See Map No. 8

Matlock Bath.

Altitude 600ft.

Adit close to Upperwood Road above Old Pavilion site. A series of old " pipe-vein " workings for lead and fluorspar once a show cave, but more recently mined. Parts are in a dangerous state.

Once known as Jacob's Cavern, also as Hopping Pipe.

References : R. V. Frost 1953, The Speleologist, Vol. I, No. 2, pp. 63-7, S.

At various times the workings have been connected with Speedwell Mine (=Royal Mine), but in difficult and confused area it is difficult to say where one ends and another starts without a survey and none is known to exist, except as above.

FOXHOLES
100663

E.C. Arch.

See Map No. 5

High Wheeldon, Earlsterndale.

Altitude 1,360ft. Length 180ft.

In small outcrop on north-west end of High Wheeldon on National Trust property. Drop 8 feet into passage leading to chamber 20 feet long where there is a branch to the right leading to third chamber and zigzag passages beyond.

Excavated remains in Buxton Museum. Further digging in progress.

References : Jackson 1952, Derbyshire Arch. Jour., Vol. XXIV, p. 72.

Gee 1958 and 1959, Peakland Arch. Soc. Newsletter, Nos. 15, 16 and 19.

FOXHOLE (Wirksworth)   **See ODIN CAVE, WIRKSWORTH**

FRANK I'TH ROCKS CAVE   E.C.

131584

Wolfscote Dale, Hartington.

Altitude 765ft. Length 150ft.

South of the footbridge in Wolfscote Dale. Two different levels one muddy and one in clean limestone. Archaeological remains in Buxton Museum.

References: L. S. Palmer 1926, Proc. Univ. Bristol Speleo. Soc., Vol. II, No. 3. J. W. Jackson 1926, N.W. Naturalist, p. 193.

FROG HOLE   M.P.

121824   See Map No. 1

Castleton.

Altitude 1,350ft. Depth 27ft.

In old quarry to north of road from Castleton to Perryfoot west of Oxlow Farm.

Digging over several years has revealed a narrow fissure dropping 6 feet into passage at head of mud filled pot, now requiring 20 feet ladder.

GATEHAM GRANGE SWALLET   Dig

116565

Near Wetton.

Altitude 830ft.

Opposite Gateham Farm. A large swallow hole. Partly excavated by Birmingham Cave and Crag Club but abandoned owing to unstable nature of walls.

GAUTRIES HOLE   V.D.C.

100814   See Map No. 1

Perryfoot, Castleton.

Altitude 1,060ft. Length 280ft.

Entrance in hollow and tree-lined plantation 200 yards north of road at Perryfoot. Permission required from Mr. Barratt, Perryfoot Farm, on opposite side of road.

Right entrance is to short dry passage only. Left entrance is to stream passage. Upstream it can be followed for only a few yards. Downstream crawl through water until it disappears down an eyehole supported with concrete. Turn right up into chamber. At top muddy chute leads into partly flooded muddy rift and back to stream and terminal sump. Return to chamber. Two holes in middle lead to small passage which increases in size after a few feet. Continue along passage to angle chamber and syphon with concrete dam. Return and climb up muddy slope on right (care—knotted rope fixed). After climb and muddy duck, passage leads to twin eyeholes and 30 feet pitch into chamber, with sump pool at bottom, containing concrete dams. Pumping and diving by B.S.A. have so far been unsuccessful.

Once known as Jackdaw Pit.

Entrance passage liable to flooding.

Tackle required : Ladder 30ft., belay 20ft., lifeline 40ft.

Reference : L. Salmon and G. Boldock 1948, Cave Science, Vol. I, No. 6, S.

GAUTRIES HILL POT   E.P.

103812   See Map No. 1

Perryfoot, Castleton.

Altitude 1,150ft. Depth 25ft.

Obvious open pot, walled round, on hillside south of Perryfoot. Scramble down east end. Opens westwards but choked immediately. Possible dig.

Also known as Coalpithole Pot.

GELLY DALE CAVES   (Bradwell)

See HARTLEDALE CAVES

GIANTS CAVE   E.C.

117827   See Map No. 1

Castleton.

Altitude 1,250ft. Length 110ft.

On west side of Peakshill, approached by track from farm road. Water emerges from low arch at south-west end of hill. A few yards to the west a short passage can be followed into the stream passage. Further round is swallet with dry cave above.

Also known as Peakshill Cave.

GIANTS CAVE (Stoney Middleton)
See BAMFORTH HOLE

Another Giants Cave at Stoney Middleton.
See Hawken Edge Cave

GIANTS HOLE   S.S.C.

119826   See Map No. 1

Castleton.

Altitude 1,250ft. Depth 495ft. Length over 10,000ft.

In hollow between Middle Hill and Peakshill, reached from track to Peakshill Farm. Permission required from farm.

Old Cave : Follow stream into obvious entrance for 100 feet, to climb and traverse into Upper Series—several rather muddy passages with a few stalactite formations. Return to stream. Continue down to Curtain (where rock comes down to 9 inches above water, or less in flood conditions). Crawl under and First Sump is soon reached. Retrace steps a few yards and climb into roof. Hole on left (looking downstream) is Pillar Crawl for about 60 feet. Drop 8 feet into sloping passage down to Backwash Pool.

Backwash Pool Dams: Bale water out of pool into a series of dams until access is possible through sump. On leaving drain dams or next party cannot bale into them. If they are full on arrival drain first to get rid of excess water and then bale out (Level should be down to outlet of first dam before baling is started). Last man should leave can on first dam to warn other parties that a party is already inside. On leaving the cave do not drain if anyone else is inside.

New Series : After the dams and sumps a short passage leads to Base Camp Chamber where river is met downstream from First Sump. Above this are chambers at high level with good formations. Continuing downstream to Garland Pot (fixed iron ladder for 30 feet) then into Giant's Crab Walk, a very narrow meandering passage for $\frac{3}{4}$ mile, with 15 feet fixed ladder at one point. Second Sump is at end of Crab Walk, and way on, is to return upstream 20 feet to passage on left into Eating House. Pass under small waterfall and along passage keeping to right at junction. This leads to St. Valentine's Sump (rarely done now as alternative route is open). Turning left at last junction leads to short crawls in narrow passage to Shatter Passage, where stream is again joined. Stream soon forms Third Sump. Walk back upstream until obvious traverse is seen on left, though great care is needed doing the traverse, which leads to

Geology Pot Series : After traverse continue along side passage to awkward 12 feet drop into chamber with 2 feet of water. Con-

40

tinue across until natural belay point is reached at head of Geology Pot (50 feet ladder required). Below passages continues again, again river is met. Continue downstream until Cascade is reached (30 feet ladder needed). Duck under curtain and down Second Cascade (30 feet ladder needed). River now forms the Canals, often impassable owing to fluctuation of water level. In low water foot of Filthy Five Pitches (from St. Valentine's Sump) can be reached.

New Upper Series: Where waterfall comes out of side passage at Eating House is entrance to upper series which leads to Crab Walk via circular tour. Awkward climb up waterfall leads to large passage, Maginn's Rift. Take small right hand passage at beginning of rift which varies considerably in height and width and has a wet crawl.

Large chamber is Ghost Rift, which should be left by small crawl at floor level. After passage with many formations is drop down into Crab Walk, which can be climbed with care though rope (60 feet) is advisable. The Crab Walk is entered a third of the way down from Garlands Pot.

Tackle required: Geology Pot, 50ft. ladder, 10ft. belay, 60ft. lifeline. Cascade, 30ft. ladder. Second Cascade, 30ft. rope. Return from Upper Series to Crab Walk, 60ft. rope. Canals, dinghy.

References: F. Atkinson 1948, Cave Science, Vol. I, No. 5, pp. 132-40, S. L. Salmon 1956, Cave Science, Vol. IV, No. 25, pp. 1-33, S. L. Salmon 1959, Cave Science, Vol. IV, No. 29, pp. 230-240, S.

GLUTTON DALE CAVE   Dig

086673   See Map No. 5

Earlsterndale.

Altitude 1,050ft. Length 30ft.

A road drain is channelled into a small cave mouth which has been dug out for 30 feet.

References: P. Smith 1960, The Lyre, Vol. I, No. 3.

GODFREY HOLE CAVE   E.C.

271536

Near Wirksworth.

Altitude 750ft. Length 70ft.

A short walk in cave immediately behind cottages of Godfreyhole hamlet. Appears to have been used as cowshed and has had two "rooms" walled off. Potentially of archaeological interest, though no report has been traced.

GOLCONDA CAVERN   In a Mine

246554

Brassington.

Altitude 1,160ft. Depth 400ft.

To the north east of Harborough Rocks in a lead mine, intermittently
working. Reached only via 400 feet deep shaft fitted with cage
and winding gear. Not normally accessible.

A large series of solution caves close to junction of limestone and
dolomites, partly sand filled. No description or survey published.

References : Farey 1811, p. 294. A very large cavern in 4th lime.
Puttrell (reprinted) 1960, Bull. Peak Dist. Mines Hist. Soc.,
Vol. I, No. 2, pp. 8-12.

GOOSEHILL CAVE   Dig ?

148827   See Map No. 1

Castleton.

Altitude 670ft. Length 15ft.

In last garden on left going up footpath behind Goosehill Hall towards Cowlow and the Winnats.

Low arch 4 feet wide and 3 feet high. Soon ends in silt choke.
Could have been old resurgence.

GORGE TOP CAVE   E.C.

150825   See Map No. 1

Castleton.

Altitude 900ft.

Rock shelter in trees by Peveril Castle Keep directly above Peak
Cavern entrance.

GREAT MASSON CAVERN   Show

292586   See Map No. 8

Matlock Bath.

Altitude 840ft. Length over 2,000ft.

Entrance close to Victoria Tower on Heights of Abraham. Largely
old lead mine with limited solutional cave at end. Entry is by
workings in Great Rake, leading into northward continuation of
Rutland (Old Nestus) Pipe Vein, with numerous worked out
vein cavities. So-called Lake is a short flooded level. Good
example of mining in pre-explosive days. Branch galleries still
being worked via Black Ox shaft. Passages lead through to open-
cast fluorspar workings and former Knowles Mine on summit of

Masson Hill, but upper end is dangerous owing to modern mine debris.

Reference: K. C. Dunham 1952, Memoir of the Geological Survey on Fluorspar, p. 99. **S.**

GREEN COWDEN CHERT QUARRY CAVE   M.C.

200678

Near Bakewell.

Altitude 870ft. Length 20ft.

In disused chert quarry, north of Bakewell-Monyash road. Small crawl passage with boulder floor goes round two bends and is then choked with boulders. A possible dig.

GREEN LANE POT   D.P.

050726   See Map No. 4

Buxton.

Altitude 1,000ft. Depth 70ft. Length 80ft.

Entrance through manhole in road outside Poole's Cavern. On descents protect hole by parking car with lights against oncoming traffic.

Wooden ladder to platform 30 feet down. Then ladder pitch 40 feet to bottom which is usually flooded to a depth of several feet. Only in drought is tube passage accessible. Apparently part of Poole's Cavern to Wye Head system. Tube is extremely muddy, being 20 inches of liquid mud in 30-inch high passage.

Tackle: Wooden ladder unsafe, use lifeline, then 25ft. ladder and lifeline. Belay on surface to car or lamp post.

Reference: Eldon Pothole Club Newsletter Vol. 5 No. 10 **S.**

GRINLOW ROCK SHELTER   E.C.

052717

Buxton.

Altitude 1,150ft. Length 10ft.

In crags halfway between Solomon's Temple and road, to south-west of Temple. Tight passage for 10 feet between boulders then too narrow. Eldon Pothole Club digging.

HADDON HOLE   D.C.

194659

Lathkilldale.

Altitude 650ft. Length 30ft.

A short crawl in the " dry " bed of the Lathkill 40 feet east of the ruined Mandale Aqueduct. Accesible only in drought, and often blocked by debris.

HANGING FLAT CAVERN   E.C.
208760   See Map No. 9

Middleton Dale.

Altitude 700ft. Length 90ft.

On north side of dale, 300 yards below Ben Bennett's Quarry 30 feet above road. Two entrances : one mined and the other natural some 30 feet above, leading into a natural cave 60 feet long, sloping upwards.

HARBOROUGH CAVE   E.C.
242552

Brassington.

Altitude 1,175ft. Length 50ft.

Obvious entrance high in Harborough Rocks above Brassington. Single chamber with chimney to surface and narrowing fissures at back. Excavated Romano-British finds in Derby Museum. Second small cave close by.

References : W. S. Fox 1909, Derbys. Arch. Jour. XXXI, pp. 89-106. J. W. Brailsford 1959, Derbys. Arch. Jour. LXXVII pp. 54-55.

HARTLEDALE CAVES   Arch. and M.C.
165803   See Map No. 2

Bradwell.

Altitude 975ft. Length 110ft.

Also known as Gelly Dale Caves.

Approach by footpath from Hartlemoor Farm or up dale from Hazle-badge. Top cave with 60 feet of crawls. Lower cave 50 feet of crawls. Entrances being re-excavated.

References : R. Pennington 1877, Quar. Jour. Geol. Soc., pp. 240-1. A. L. Pill 1963, Cave Science, Vol. V, No. 33.

HARVEYDALE QUARRY TUBES   V.D.C.
296598   See Map No. 8

Matlock.

Altitude 350ft.

In working quarry, variously known as Harveydale, Holt or Hope Quarry. Four tubes, A, B, C and D from north to south, all 30-50 feet above quarry floor and sometimes difficult of access.

A. Length 1,500ft. V.D.C. Long crawl in bedding tube with low meander channel often only way through. At 375 feet from entrance cross passage. Right is long wet crawl. Left is walking to another junction. Left (down-dip) is dangerously tight and deceptive. Right leads out into side of deep mine shaft on Seven Rakes Vein, with water 65 feet below.

B. Too tight for entry.

C. Hands and knees crawl for 300 feet in a westerly direction to a small shaft 30 feet deep. Cross this and a further 300 feet leads to same shaft as in tube A but 30 feet higher.

D. Not explored owing to quarry workings.

References : Op Mole reports for 1958-9. Reprinted in British Caver, Vol. XXXI.

HAWKEN EDGE CAVE   E.C.

218757   See Map No. 9

Middleton Dale.

Altitude 620ft. Length 52ft.

At west end of Dalton's Quarry on south side of dale, 50 feet above road, by side of path to Lane Head.

Large entrance 15 feet high. Soon closes.

Quarrying in progress around entrance.

HAYHOLE   D.C.

106540   See Map No. 7

Manifold Valley.

Altitude 700ft.

Also known as Jack Daw's Hole.

A crescent shaped opening high in the face of Beeston Tor, which can only be entered by descending on a rope or ladder and swinging in. No extension known. Wind-blown material on floor.

HAZLEBADGE CAVE   M.C.

171801   See Map No. 2

Bradwell.

Altitude 720ft. Length 100ft. Depth 30ft.

Entrance below small crag on hill spur north of Hazlebadge Hall 180 feet east of road.

Entrance requires 25 feet ladder or rope for good climbers. Short rope useful for scrambles ahead. Ends in stalagmited choke, a possible dig. To right is crawl to small chamber. In roof of main passage are miners wooden stemples which should NOT be climbed.

Farey's cave at HAZLEBADGE was probably Quarter's Farm Swallet not the above   (See Farey 1811, p. 296).

HERMIT'S CAVE

E.C.

227623

Near Birchover, in Cratcliffe Tor.

Altitude 800ft.

A semi-artificial enlarged joint in gritstone. Formerly used by a hermit who carved a Crucifixion in the wall. Now used by climbers as a shelter.

HIGH TOR GROTTO

M.C.

296588   See Map No. 8

Matlock Bath.

Altitude 350ft.   Length 300ft.

North of the Paint Works on the east bank of the Derwent. A former show cave with good calcite crystals. Entry by permission from Paint Works.

HILLOCKS MINE

M.P.

145672   See Map No. 3

Monyash.

Altitude 950ft.   Length ½ mile.

In field south-east of junction of green lanes, ¾ mile north-west of Monyash. Formerly known as Whalf Mine or Whalf Pipe. Roomy entrance series, walking for 600 feet. Flat out crawl leads to 12 feet scramble down to First Coffin Level 60 feet long. At end is First Pitch, 30 feet. Belay to piton in floor or to beam at entrance to coffin level. Scramble down spiral passages to Second Pitch. Belay should be threaded through small hole and taken up and over to head of pitch proper. Pitch tricky for novices as it ends on slope of boulders descending some 30 feet. Alternative route by going ahead at head of pitch, back and footing halfway down shaft and crawl back underneath. Not recommended. At bottom low arch enters lower levels. High and wide passages with good mineralisation. Old winding shaft still visible. One branch ends in blind sump. Another in partly collapsed caverns. Another in old workings.

			Ladder.	Belay.	Lifeline.
Tackle :	1st pitch	...	35ft.	10ft. or 70ft.	50ft.
	2nd pitch	...	35ft.	20ft.	50ft.

References : J. C. Gilbert 1953, Cave Science, Vol. III, No. 21, p. 223, S. J. Robey 1961-3, Bull. Peak Dist. Mines Hist. Soc., Vol. I, Nos. 5 and 6, Vol. II, No. 1, S.

HIPLEY DALE ROCK SHELTER   E.C.

210543

Near Brassington.

Altitude 650ft. Length 15ft.

Two obvious shelters on south side of dale close to Bakewell-Ashbourne road, broken into by quarrying. One has good bedding anastomosis.

HOB'S HOUSE CAVE   E.C.

175708

Monsal Dale

Altitude 800ft. Length 80ft.

A narrow descending fissure at the back of the landslips. A human skeleton of early British date was found among the debris at the bottom but no attempt at excavation has been recorded.

Reference : W. S. Fox 1913, Derbyshire Arch. Jour. XXXV (with location plan).

Also known as Hob Thirst Hole, Hob Hurst House or Hob's Hurst Cave, and often confused with Thirst House in Deepdale, with descriptions of one cave applied to the other, etc.

Also known as Monsal Dale Cave.

HOBBIT HOLE

204760

Altitude 750ft. Length 35ft.

Middleton Dale.

In Ben Bennett's Quarry, 200 feet north-west of the Time Office. Sometimes inaccessible owing to gravel tipping.

A short old resurgence cave.

HOE GRANGE QUARRY CAVE

223560

Brassington.

Altitude 1,100ft.

Now completely quarried away. Yielded Pleistocene mammal remains. Quarry now disused and exhibits a variety of solution features along joints and bedding.

References: Bemrose and Newton 1905, Quar. Jour. Geol. Soc. LXI, pp. 43-62, S.

HOGSLAND CAVERN
About 355622

In a Mine

Milltown, Ashover.

A cavern struck in the workings down the Hogsland lead mine shaft and now under water. Exact position not known but believed to be under east side of Fall Hill, in a series of pipe-vein workings some 200 feet below the surface.

HORSESHOE CAVE (Castleton)

See SUICIDE CAVE

HUBBERDALE PIPE CAVERNS
1469

Closed

Sough Tail shaft in Deepdale 161695

Monyash area.

A pipe vein said to be 150 yards wide running a little west of north intersected by the level from Deepdale at 46 fathoms depth. No details known and all shafts and level blocked (the latter about 1,000 feet in). Old accounts suggest that it would be very extensive and interesting if access could be gained.

Reference : The Lyre 1958, Vol. I, No. 2, pp. 54-68.

HUNGER HILL SWALLOW
209770

See Map No. 9

Eyam.

Altitude 920ft.

In field 70 yards west of Hunger Hill Farm. A large rift-like collapsed shakehole, some 70 feet by 30 feet, choked with farm rubbish. Could be dug.

ILAM ROCK CAVE
142531

E.C.

See Map No. 6

Altitude 525ft. Length 30ft.

Dovedale.

Inside the detached Ilam Rock Entrance 4 feet high rising to 30 feet inside. Overhanging walls have much tufa inside.

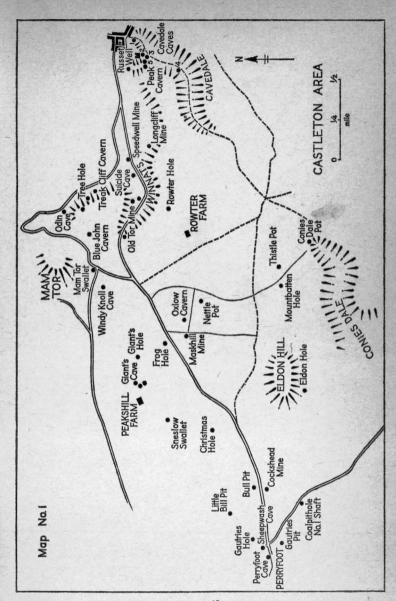

Map No.1

CASTLETON AREA

N

0   ¼   ½
    mile

CAVEDALE

Cavedale Caves

Russet Well

Peak 5 3 2

Peak Cavern

Longcliff Mine

Speedwell Mine

Suicide Cave

Treak Cliff Cavern

Tree Hole

Odin Cave

WINNAT'S

Old Tor Mine

Blue John Cavern

Rowter Hole

ROWTER FARM

MAM TOR

Mam Tor Swallet

Windy Knoll Cave

Giant's Cave   Giant's Hole

Frog Hole

PEAKSHILL FARM

Oxlow Cavern

Nettle Pot

Maskhill Mine

Thistle Pot

Conies Dale Pot

Mountbatten Hole

ELDON HILL

Eldon Hole

CONIES DALE

Sneslow Swallet

Christmas Hole

Little Bill Pit

Bull Pit

Cockshead Mine

Gautries Hole

Perryfoot Cave   Sheepwash Cave

PERRYFOOT

Gautries Pit

Coalpithole No.1 Shaft

49

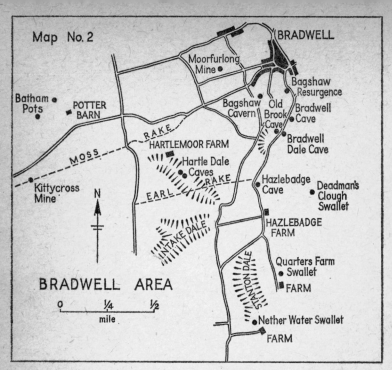

Map No. 2

BRADWELL

Moorfurlong Mine

Bagshaw Resurgence

Batham Pots

POTTER BARN

Bagshaw Cavern

Old Brook Cave

Bradwell Cave

RAKE

HARTLEMOOR FARM

Bradwell Dale Cave

MOSS

Hartle Dale Caves

RAKE

Hazlebadge Cave

Deadman's Clough Swallet

Kittycross Mine

EARL

N

HAZLEBADGE FARM

INTAKE DALE

Quarters Farm
Swallet

FARM

BRADWELL AREA

STANTON DALE

0   ¼   ½
mile

Nether Water Swallet

FARM

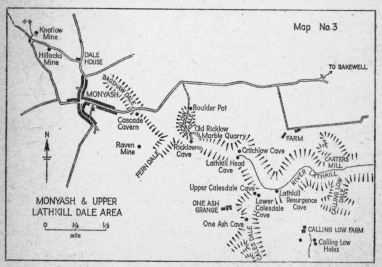

Map No. 3

Knotlow Mine

Hillocks Mine

DALE HOUSE

TO BAKEWELL

BAGSHAW DALE

MONYASH

Boulder Pot

Cascade Cavern

Old Ricklow
Marble Quarry

FARM

N

Raven Mine

FERN DALE

Ricklow
Cave

Critchlow Cave

CARTERS MILL

Lathkill Head
Cave

RIVER LATHKILL

CALLING LOW DALE

MONYASH & UPPER
LATHKILL DALE AREA

Upper Calesdale Cave

ONE ASH
GRANGE

Lower
Calesdale
Cave

Lathkill
Resurgence
Cave

0   ¼   ½
mile

One Ash Cave

CALES DALE

CALLING LOW FARM

Calling Low
Holes

50

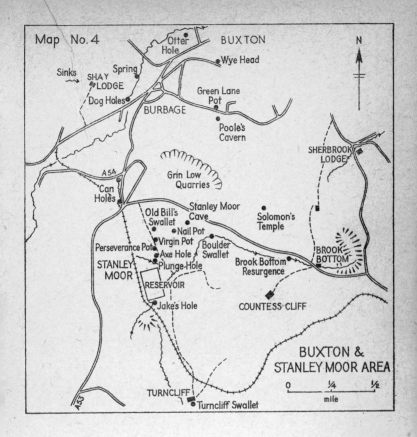

BUXTON

Otter Hole

Wye Head

Sinks

Spring

SHAY LODGE

Dog Holes

Green Lane Pot

BURBAGE

Poole's Cavern

SHERBROOK LODGE

Grin Low Quarries

A54

Can Holes

Old Bill's Swallet

Stanley Moor Cave

Solomon's Temple

Nail Pot

Virgin Pot

BROOK BOTTOM

Perseverance Pot

Boulder Swallet

Axe Hole

STANLEY MOOR

Plunge-Hole

Brook Bottom Resurgence

RESERVOIR

Jake's Hole

COUNTESS CLIFF

BUXTON & STANLEY MOOR AREA

0   ¼   ½
mile

TURNCLIFF

Turncliff Swallet

A53

IVY GREEN CAVE

M.C.

223757

See Map No. 9

Middleton Dale.

Altitude 680ft.   Length 350ft.

High up in cliffs opposite old Brampton Mill, on north side of dale, immediately west of where Cliff Style Rake breaks into the Dale. A stream passage cave trending west-north-west, parallel and higher than Carlswork.

Accessible only by rock-climbing above two mine levels.

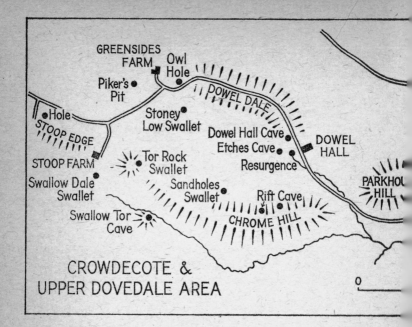

GREENSIDES
FARM
Owl
Hole
Piker's
Pit
Hole
STOOP EDGE
STOOP FARM
Swallow Dale
Swallet
Stoney
Low Swallet
Tor Rock
Swallet
Sandholes
Swallet
Swallow Tor
Cave
DOWEL DALE
Dowel Hall Cave
Etches Cave
Resurgence
DOWEL
HALL
Rift Cave
CHROME HILL
PARKHOU
HILL

CROWDECOTE &
UPPER DOVEDALE AREA

0

JACOB'S CAVERN (Matlock Bath)

Alternative name for FLUORSPAR CAVERN, also name of one
chamber in the cave.

Reference : Bemrose 1910, " Derbyshire," p. 46.

JACKDAW'S HOLE (Beeston Tor)

See HAYHOLE

JAKES HOLE

V.D.P.

044709

See Map No. 4

Stanley Moor, Buxton.

Altitude 1,250ft. Depth 35ft. Length 80ft.

In deep shakehole near south wall of Stanley Moor Reservoir. Shakehole has large limestone slab at one side. Tight 6 feet crawl
down slope. Squeeze over boulder to top of 25 feet pitch. Very
tight. Belay iron bar in floor. 10 feet square chamber at bottom
is very muddy. Tight squeeze into 20 feet silted passage on left.

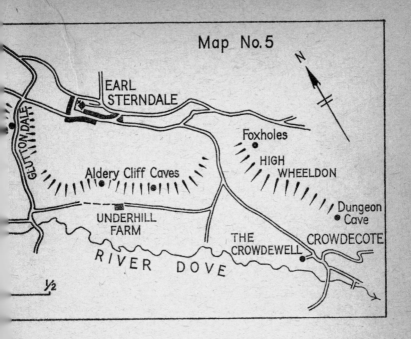

Map No. 5

EARL STERNDALE

GLUTTON DALE

Foxholes

HIGH WHEELDON

Aldery Cliff Caves

Dungeon Cave

UNDERHILL FARM

THE CROWDEWELL

CROWDECOTE

RIVER DOVE

½

Whole cave uninteresting and difficult to get out of! Suitable only for thin agile cavers.

Tackle: 25ft. ladder, 50ft. lifeline.

Jakes Hole (Lower)

In same shakehole where a small stream sinks along boulders. This has been dug and penetrated for 20 feet but is now considered impossible for further work.

Reference: Eldon Pothole Club Newsletter Vol. 5, No. 10.

JUG HOLES   D.C.

279595   See Map No. 8

Matlock.

Altitude 850ft. Length over ½ mile.

In wood south of Leawood Farm and north of Salters Lane on summit of Masson Hill. Large cave entrance in wood leads to workings ahead and to left. On right near foot of slope is descent into series of muddy caverns, with branches to old workings, and

53

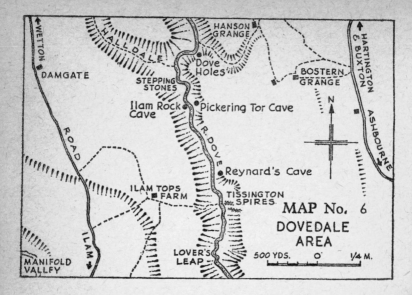

MAP No. 6
DOVEDALE AREA

500 YDS.   0   1/4 M.

finally out to adit entrance lower down hill. At back and to right 12 feet shaft leads to Boulder Maze on left and to roomy but dirty stalagmite caverns with limestone roof and floor of green clay-decomposed basalt lava. Once noted for its bats and for the "sound of a barking dog" caused by a small syphon pool no longer operative.

At present mining is in progress at the entrance and both lower adit entrance and shaft to Stalagmite caverns are blocked.

Reference: D. Nash 1957, Trans. Cave Research Group, Vol. V, No. 1.

KINDERLOW CAVERN   M.C.

072867

Edale.

Altitude 1,800ft.

¼ mile east of shooting hut near top of Oaken Clough on Kinderscout. In gritstone, entrance among tumbled blocks difficult to find. A series of fissures in the gritstone.

KITTYCROSS CAVERN   Via Mine

151803   See Map No. 2

Bradwell Moor.

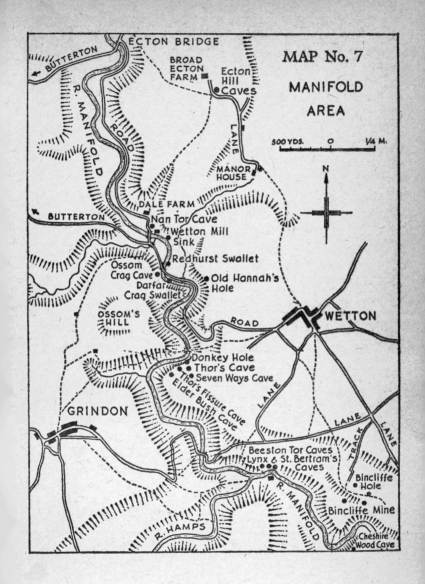

MAP No. 7

MANIFOLD

AREA

500 YDS.   0   ¼ M.

N

ECTON BRIDGE

BUTTERTON

BROAD
ECTON
FARM

Ecton
Hill
Caves

R. MANIFOLD

ROAD

LANE

MANOR
HOUSE

BUTTERTON

DALE FARM

Nan Tor Cave

Wetton Mill
Sink

Redhurst Swallet

Ossom
Crag Cave

Darfar
Crag Swallet

Old Hannah's
Hole

OSSOM'S
HILL

ROAD

WETTON

Donkey Hole

Thor's Cave

Seven Ways Cave

Thor's Fissure Cave

Elder Bush Cave

GRINDON

LANE

LANE

Beeston Tor Caves

Lynx & St. Bertram's
Caves

TRACK

LANE

Bincliffe
Hole

R. MANIFOLD

Bincliffe Mine

R. HAMPS

Cheshire
Wood Cave

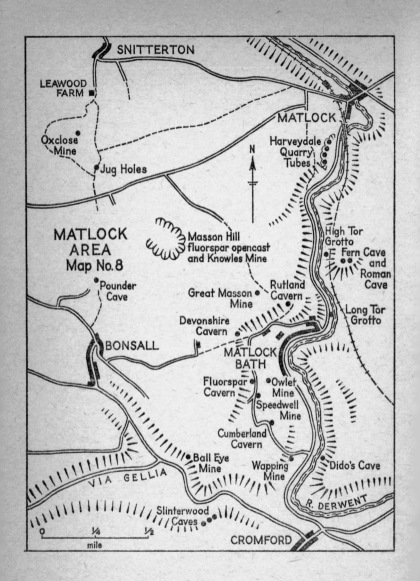

SNITTERTON

LEAWOOD
FARM

Oxclose
Mine

Jug Holes

MATLOCK

Harveydale
Quarry
Tubes

N

MATLOCK
AREA
Map No. 8

Masson Hill
fluorspar opencast
and Knowles Mine

Pounder
Cave

Great Masson
Mine

Rutland
Cavern

High Tor
Grotto

Fern Cave
and
Roman
Cave

Devonshire
Cavern

Long Tor
Grotto

BONSALL

MATLOCK
BATH

Fluorspar
Cavern

Owlet
Mine

Speedwell
Mine

Cumberland
Cavern

Ball Eye
Mine

Wapping
Mine

Dido's Cave

VIA GELLIA

R. DERWENT

Slinterwood
Caves

0   ¼   ½
        mile

CROMFORD

At bottom of 450 feet deep mine shaft east of Moss Rake washing plant. Short natural fissure with 10 feet drop leads into single chamber in top of decomposed lava.

Reference : T. D. Ford 1951, British Caver, Vol. XXII, pp. 45-8, S.

KNOTLOW MINE and CAVERN D.P.

144674 See Map No. 3

Monyash.

Altitude 960ft. Length about 3,000ft.

Opened by Eccles Caving Club 1959.

Climbing shaft entrance about 100 feet north-east of Second Stile along the Taddington footpath from the junction of the Green Lanes north-west of Monyash. Covered by concrete slab and steel lid. Permission and key obtainable from Mr. F. Goodwin, Town End Farm, Monyash.

Entrance shaft 60ft. Short slope to Second pitch 25 feet, belayed to end of First Ladder. This enters Pearl Chamber, and main cave runs back under entrance shaft in bedding cave with partial fill of deads leaving a narrow walk-way in the middle. Several short descents and then dangerous descent down jammed boulders for 30 feet. Across chamber on left is crawl followed by 10 feet chimney down to both mined and natural passages. Almost immediately in these is long East Level—a coffin level, probably the finest still preserved in Derbyshire, which ends in a vein blockage, in process of clearance. Upstream beyond East Level is crawl into natural cave system via very tight hole " The Bung " and 400 feet crawl to the Standing Room. Two crawls lead off; one back over north-east passage to a vertical rift which can be climbed for about 30 feet. Forward from the Standing Room the other crawl passes the foot of the Great Aven and continues very tight into Rumble Chamber where digging is still in progress.

Returning to the boulder descent, continue down to a mine level which leads to the top of the Waterfall Chamber with a 50 feet pitch to the lower levels, partly coffin levels, and often flooded to within a few inches of the roof. Main level goes to foot of Fourways Shaft. Left leads to Engine Shaft. Ahead is North level abandoned after reaching Hill Shaft. The right hand passage takes the drainage via a coffin level to Rift Chamber where the continuation is blocked, though water can be heard falling ahead at times. Amphibious digging is required ! More water enters Rift Chamber, probably from East Level and Hillocks Mine. A dam is under construction to assist digging.

Descents may be made via Engine Shaft or Fourways shaft, both 200 feet deep, with long belays to trees needed. In case of accident in the lower levels these could be used, but the entrance shaft

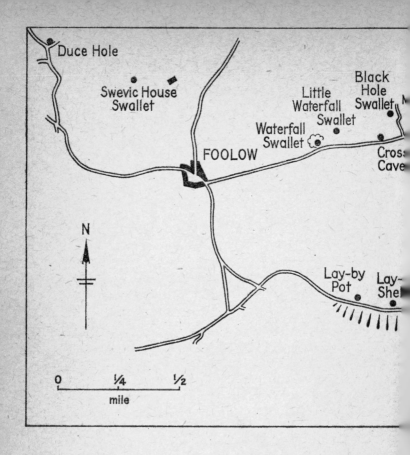

Duce Hole

Swevic House
Swallet

Little
Waterfall
Swallet

Black
Hole
Swallet

Waterfall
Swallet

FOOLOW

Cross
Cave

N

Lay-by
Pot

Lay-
She

0   ¼   ½
mile

would be better for someone injured in the upper levels.   It would be very difficult to get any injured person through the Bung.

Tackle : Entrance pitch ladder 60ft., Lifeline 80ft. belay to bolts under lid.

2nd pitch ladder 25ft., lifeline 30ft. Belay to foot of first ladder.

3rd pitch (Waterfall) 50ft., lifeline 50ft., belay 30ft.

References : B. Saville 1960, The Lyre, Vol. I, No. 3, **S.** J. Robey 1961-3, Bull. Peak Dist. Mines Hist. Soc., Vol. I, Nos. 5 and 6, Vol. II, No. 1.

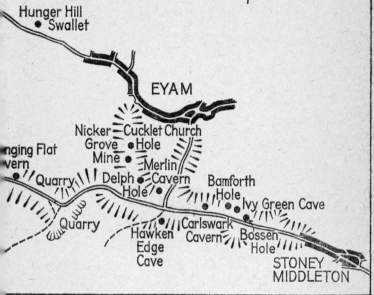

STONEY MIDDLETON & EYAM AREA

Map No. 9

Hunger Hill
• Swallet

EYAM

Nicker—Cucklet Church
Grove •Hole
Mine • —Merlin
Delph ≠Cavern
Hole
Bamforth
Hole
Ivy Green Cave

nging Flat
vern
• Quarry

Quarry
Hawken
Edge
Cave
Carlswark
Cavern
Bossen
Hole
STONEY
MIDDLETON

KNOWLES MINE CAVERNS

286591 See Map No. 8

Matlock.

Altitude 1,050ft.

A series of partly sand-filled old solution caves formerly reached via Knowles Mine adit but now breached by open-cast workings on the summit of Masson Hill. Connection established with King Mine and Great Masson Cavern. The parts accessible vary according to the state of mining.

References : Farey 1811, p. 294. Dunham 1952, Memoir of the Geological Survey on Fluorspar, p. 99.

LADMANLOW CAVERN

Buxton.

Probably an old name for Plunge Hole.—See British Caver for 1950.
Vol. 20, p. 73.

LANGWITH CAVE   Arch.

517695

Upper Langwith.

Near Cresswell.

Single chamber with two short passages. Neolithic burial.

References : E. H. Mullins 1913, Derbys. Arch. Jour. XXXV, pp.
137-158, S. Geological Survey Memoir 1913, Northern Part of
Derbyshire Coalfield.

LAMB POTS   Digs ?

100795

Peak Forest.

Altitude 1,150-1,200ft. Depth 30-60ft.

A series of 7 open natural shafts on the hillside $\frac{1}{4}$ mile west of
Chamber Farm, west of Peak Forest. All choked at depths of
30-60 feet with boulders. Other pots on same hillside choked
to surface.

LATHKILL HEAD CAVE   D.C.

171659   See Map No. 3

Lathkilldale.

Altitude 700ft. Length 1,000ft.

Also known as Lathkill House Cavern and incorrectly as Ricklow
Cavern.

The only large obvious entrance in upper Lathkilldale. Resurgence
of the river in wet weather, 20 feet high entrance soon reduces
to a 200 feet crawl over large slabs. Ahead leads to two Rift
Chambers and spiral down amongst boulders into bedding caves
and into stream way, largely crawling on mud and sand for 100
feet or so either up or downstream, has been forced further down
in time of drought. Upstream scramble over boulders and into
fissure leads up into Puttrells Chamber. Upper rift chambers
are very unstable and best left alone.

CARE : Observe landmarks at all junctions for return journey—it is easy to get lost—and the whole lower series floods in wet weather !

References : H. A. Bamber 1948, Cave Science, Vol. I, No. 5. H. A. Bamber 1951, Cave Science, Vol. II, No. 15, S.

LATHKILL RESURGENCE CAVE   V.D.C.

176654   See Map No. 3

Lathkilldale.

Altitude 650ft. Length 200-300ft.

Entered during 1959 drought. About 1 mile downdale from Lathkill Head Cave, below waterfall, known as Bubble Springs. Entrance (and probably most of cave) normally under water, and choked with debris. Long bedding crawl with small chambers, eventually becoming too low.

Reference : S. Gee 1956, The Lyre, Vol. I, No. 2, S.

LAY-BY POT   E.C.

202760   See Map No. 9

Middleton Dale.

Altitude 830ft. Length 20ft.

On north side of dale, opposite second lay-by coming from Wardlow. Behind earth bank and vegetation.

Short mined passage slopes down into aven, with dirty stalactite above and pot 2 feet wide with 8 feet deep below, at present choked with rubbish.

LAY-BY SHELTER   E.C.

205760   See Map No. 9

Middleton Dale.

Altitude 800ft.

Immediately west of Hanging Flat Mine.

Opposite third lay-by down dale from Wardlow, large entrance easily visible to west-bound traffic. Soon closes down to flat-out crawls, which are not known to have been fully explored. Only a thin man can get in.

LEE HOUSE QUARRY CAVE   Arch. Dig ?

086503

Waterhouses.

Altitude 730ft.

Cave entrance high in disused Lee House Quarry on north east of
village. Difficult of access and roof unstable but easily visible
and has cave-earth fill just inside awaitnig excavation.

May be the same as Waterhouses Fissure recorded by Heath 1882,
Derbys. Arch. Jour., pp. 164-5. Brown 1864-5, Trans. Midland
Scientific Assn., p. 34.

LITTLE BULL PIT   E.P. Dig

104817   See Map No. 1

Castleton.

Altitude 1,100ft.   Depth 25ft.

Swallet passage at present being dug, under open pot with mud floor
and crawls under walls in places. Another dig in progress in
open pit.

References : Salmon and Boldock 1950, Cave Science, No. 11. Eldon
Pothole Club Newsletter, Vol. V, No. 4.

LONGCLIFFE FISSURE

Brassington.

See Rains Cave. An archaeological dig.

LONGCLIFF CAVERNS   See ROWTER
HOLE, Castleton

LONGCLIFF MINE and POT   D.P.

141825   See Map No. 1

Castleton.

Altitude 1,000ft.   Depth 150ft.

Shaft on highest prominent hillock on hillside behind Speedwell
Cavern leads through roof of natural pot. Workings and a second
short pitch extend some 200 feet eastwards. Main shaft temporarily blocked by caving in of hillock, and ginging unstable at top.

Tackle : 130ft. ladder and lifeline and beam for belay. 30ft.
rope for 2nd pitch and traverse.

Reference : Ford 1962, Bull. Peak Dist. Mines Hist. Soc., Vol. I, No.
7, S.

LONG TOR GROTTO   M.C.

297586   See Map No. 8

Matlock Bath.

Altitude 300ft.   Length 300ft.

Entrance below wicket gate on river bank just north of footbridge to paint works. Sough tunnel westwards under main road. Series of old workings in Great Rake with solutional effects in bedding, etc. Difficult to understand why this was called a Grotto, though it was apparently open to visitors at one time.

LORDS and LADIES MINE   M.C.

270605

Wensley.

Altitude 600ft.

On east side of Northern Dale, between Wensley and Snitterton. A series of old lead mine workings which have intersected several small solution caves.

Reference: D. Nash 1957, Trans. Cave Research Group, Vol. V, No. 1.

LUDCHURCH CAVERN   E.C.

987657

Near Wincle, Cheshire.

Altitude 1,050ft.

A partly open fissure in gritstone, of impressive size.

LUDWELL SPRING

124625

Dovedale.

Altitude 750ft.

Large resurgence from boulders by road. Short mine level nearby with good flowstone. A possible dig.

LUMB HOLE   M.C.

173733

Cressbrook.

Altitude 630ft.

Also known as Cressbrookdale Resurgence.

Obvious resurgence in floor of Cressbrook Gorge, only just above a lava bed. Possible to crawl in some 30 feet, blocked by large boulders.

Crawl passages in cliff above total 200 feet.

Old dry cave in cliff opposite.

Reference : R. V. Frost 1956, The Speleologist, Vol. I, No. 4.

LYNX CAVE

See Map No. 7

D.C.

106540

Manifold Valley.

Altitude 650ft. Length 150ft.

140 feet above river on Beeston Tor, below river junction. Short passage enters chamber with remains of good formations.

Tight crawl 35 feet from end.

Excavated—remains were all of Lynx.

A few feet to the east is Lower Lynx Cave where polecat and reindeer bones were found.

Finds in Natural History Museum, London.

Reference : G. H. Wilson 1926, Some Caves and Crags of Peakland, pp. 54-58.

MAGPIE MINE

Mine

Shaft 172682   Sough 179696

Sheldon, Bakewell.

Altitude (Sough Tail 480ft.). Length about 1 mile.

Engine shaft nearly 600 feet deep still fitted with cage, etc., and dangerous climbing ladders. Sough over a mile long about half of it waist deep, with interesting lock-gates and water feeders in the veins. Blende vein, 600 yards north of shaft has series of calcite lined pipe-vein cavities which have been pirated by a solution channel in places, which can be followed for about 100 yards and could perhaps be dug out further. Extensive workings in vein under shaft.

"Chatsworth Cavern" was a large vein cavity now completely submerged.

Sough Tail on south bank of River Wye, west of Ashford, opposite Black Rock Corner. Partly collapsed at present.

MAM TOR SWALLET

M.P.

128832

See Map No. 1

Castleton.

Altitude 1,250ft. Length 100ft. Depth 60ft.

A series of short pitches with chambers between. Sump in middle level leads nowhere. Stream sinks in impenetrable fissure. 60 feet rope advisable for return. Stream believed to reappear in Blue John Caverns to east.

Used as dump for dead sheep !

Reference : B. Saville 1959, The Lyre, Vol. I, No. 3.

MANDALE MINE

Mine

197661

Lathkilldale.

Altitude 550ft. Length about ¼ mile now accessible.

One of the oldest lead mines in Derbyshire. Incline entrance at cliff foot leads into main level, usually knee deep in water. Various old stopes can be reached along it, and evidence of sand filled solution cavities seen in places. Sough tail by footpath can be followed under old engine house but is blocked beyond. Workings reputed to extend 1 mile to north-west.

Reference : J. Rieuwerts 1963, Bull Peak Dist. Mines Hist. Soc., Vol. II, No. 1, S.

MANIFOLD CAVE (Perryfoot)   See SHEEPWASH CAVE

MANYSTONES QUARRY CAVES

237551

Longcliffe, Brassington.

Altitude 1,050ft.

A large disused limestone quarry has a small blind solution cave on the left near the entrance. In the lower northern part of the quarry are several small solution tubes high up. One appears to be large enough for entry (and excavation of mud fill ?) but will require scaling ladders to reach it.

The hill between the quarry and Longcliffe is unnamed on the 6-inch map but was once known as Waterlow and is presumed to be the site of " extensive caverns " entered via an old mine shaft as reported in an untraceable newspaper cutting, apparently written by Puttrell or Baker some 60 years ago, and called by them " Waterlow Caverns."

MASKHILL MINE

S.S.P.

125824

See Map No. 1

Castleton.

Altitude 1,430ft. Depth 450ft.

The alternative entrance to Oxlow Caverns (see under) situated 200 yards west of Oxlow Caverns entrance. A mine shaft surrounded by wire fencing and covered with wooden beams. Part mine and part pothole. Entrance pitch 120 feet to slope where 50 feet of handline is required, leading to large chamber with 8 feet drop. After chamber is long scree slope with 25 feet pitch at bottom. Long belay required to flake at top of scree slope. At the foot of this pitch is Murmuring Churn, and belay for next pitch of 80 feet is metal spike on sloping ledge which requires care. When anyone is climbing 80 feet pitch no one must move on scree above 25 feet pitch or loose material will fall down both! At foot of 80 feet pitch mine workings continue and great care should be taken amongst deads. Next pitch is 30 feet followed by climb down two 12 feet shafts. Large chamber can then be seen through eyehole but way on is 80 feet pitch through hole in floor with no obvious belay. This pitch is well-watered and ends at head of last pitch in Waterfall Chamber of Oxlow Caverns. Continuation may be made down 35 feet pitch (in recently collapsed floor) and 12 feet pitch to final sump.

Tackle required :

			Ladder.	Belay.	Lifeline.
			ft.	ft.	ft.
First pitch	...	...	120	10	130
Slope	...	...		50 handline	
Second pitch	...	...	25	100	50
Third pitch	...	...	80	10	100
Fourth (Murmuring Churn)	...		30	20	50
Fifth (into Oxlow)		...	80	30	100
Sixth (Waterfall Chamber)	...		35	20	50
Seventh (to Sump)		...	12	10	—

Great care must be taken throughout owing to loose rocks. It must not be tackled by inexperienced persons, but for those with experience a round trip into Oxlow and out of Maskhill or vice versa is possible.

Permission must be obtained from Oxlow House Farm.

Reference : Salmon and Boldock 1951, Cave Science, Vol. III, No. 17, pp. 13-30, S.

MASSON CAVERN

Matlock Bath.

See Great Masson Mine and Knowles Mine Cavern.

MERLIN'S CAVE

M.C.

218759

See Map No. 9

Eyam.

Altitude 680ft.   Length 1,000ft.

West side of Eyam Dale near where it joins the main Tideswell road. Ordinary mine entrance, an enlarged fissure. Gated and access controlled by Peak District Mines Historical Society. Old show cave, containing little natural stuff and has wooden steps for ascent of slope. Not too safe as roof is packed on wooden stemples. 30 feet shaft at end is blind. Numerous scrambles in roof. Good sporting cave.

References : J. Rieuwerts 1960, Bull. Peak Dist. Mines Hist. Soc., Vol. I, No. 2, S. B. King 1962, Cave Sci., Vol. IV, No. 32, p. 380, S.

MIDDLETON DALE ROCK SHELTER   E.C.

209759

Middleton Dale.

Altitude 690ft. Length 30ft.

On north side of dale, 500 yards below Ben Bennett's Quarry, opposite the explosives store.

A rock shelter with two small tubes extending 20 and 30 feet from western end.

MILLCLOSE MINE   E.P.

Shaft 259625   Sough 266624

Darleybridge.

Altitude 400ft. Depth.   Length over ½ mile.

Situated just over one mile north-east of Darleybridge. Entrance to the mine is strictly by permission from the owners, H. J. Enthoven and Sons Ltd., **prior to visit.**

Boarded over and locked, the entrance shaft is situated in the outbuildings and has fixed iron ladders to the only accessible level at a depth of 60 feet. The shaft continues down over 800 feet but is full of water and boarded over. From the shaft and passage leads to a T junction. Right at this junction leads to a water-filled passage and old pumping shaft which is **not boarded over.**

Left at the T junction leads to Yatestoop Sough along which water rushes to the exit and into the River Derwent.

Interesting ochreous deposits in roof and on sides of passage of sough. Sough passage can be followed into mine until roof fall prevents progress. Very strong current of water pours over top of roof fall. Flooded caverns below water-table contained linings of lead ore, etc.

MONSAL DALE CAVE   E.C.

175708   **See HOB THIRST HOLE**

MOORFURLONG MINE and CAVERNS   M.P.

168812   See Map No. 2

Bradwell.

Altitude 820ft. Length 700ft. Depth 70ft

Reference : A. L. Marsh 1953, Speleologist, Vol. 1, 3-8, S.

50 feet entrance pitch. Short passage leads to Second Pitch 12 feet. At foot series of pipe workings and natural caverns extends to south-east and north-west. South-east is longer series running some 600 feet and bending round to the east, via old Buddle Pools and " The Vice " crawl. To the north-west of the entrance is about 100 feet of bedding cave.

MOSS POT and CAVE (Bradwell Moor)
See BATHAM POT

MOTHER GRUNDY'S PARLOUR   E.C.
534741

Creswell.

Altitude 280ft.

Under Creswell Crags. Crawl under blocks. Contains small chamber.

Flints and bones excavated can be seen in British Museum, London.
References : Armstrong 1936 onwards, in Derbyshire Arch. Jour.

Geological Survey Memoir 1913, N. Part of Derbyshire Coalfield, p. 108.

MOULDRIDGE MINE   Mine and E.C.
194595

Gratton Dale.

Altitude 900ft. Length 500ft.

Obvious mine level by tips in south branch of upper Gratton Dale. Mine was worked during last war. A pipe-vein with mineralised solution cavities. Several open mine shafts nearby into lower workings, of unknown extent.

MOUNTBATTEN POT   Dig
127812   See Map No. 1

Altitude 1,480ft. Depth 110ft.

Castleton.

Narrow natural fissure ¼ mile south of Nettle Pot, which has been dug out to a small calcited chamber. Metal lid on top.

110 feet ladder and lifeline required. Very tight and should be attempted by agile cavers only.

Also known as Nettle Shaft Pot.

NAIL POT   M.C.

045715   See Map No. 4

Buxton.

Altitude 1,250ft.   Depth 50ft.   Length c.50ft.

50 yards south of Stanley Moor Cave.   Approximately 50 feet of passages.   Partly collapsed in 1962 and now filled in for safety.

Reference: Eldon Pothole Club Newsletter Vol. 5, No. 10, **S.**

NAN TOR CAVE   E.C.

095562   See Map No. 7

Manifold.

Altitude 640ft.   Map No. 18.

Just north of Wetton Mill Farm, on National Trust property.   Limestone hummock riddled with holes from which one can emerge
in most unexpected places.

Permit to visit required.

NETHERWATER SWALLET

171791   See Map No. 2

Bradwell Dale.

Altitude 790ft.

A choked swallet 100 yards below Netherwater Farm and immediately below the Fluorspar Mine.   It has been used in attempts
to dispose of water pumped from the mine, though it is also
thought that it leads flood waters into the mine.   Water probably
goes to Bagshaw Cavern.

NETTLE POT   S.S.P.

125820   See Map No. 1

Castleton.

Altitude 1,450ft.   Depth 520ft.

Off Sparrowpit road ½ mile south of Oxlow House Farm, but best
approached from lane leaving Sparrowpit-Castleton road near
Eldon Hill Quarry.   Permission must be obtained from Oxlow
House Farm.

Entrance was dug out by Derbyshire Pennine Club in 1934.

First Pitch is very tight and awkward to rig.   Follow instructions care-
fully.   Belay 60 feet of ladder to metal frame of lid and send two
men down to Sentry Box, below the Narrows.   Next add 120 feet

of ladder to top of 60 feet and with assistance from below thread in through to foot of Bottle Pitch. Separate belay for lower 120 feet can then be arranged at Sentry Box. A few feet from bottom of entrance pitch is Grand Canyon Pitch requiring 25 feet ladder followed by 50 feet handline for traverse past top of

Elizabeth Shaft. Great care needed. From bottom of Grand Canyon Elizabeth may be descended either direct through small hole by winch by 180 feet ladder from old winch or through large hole in two pitches of 90 and 100 feet. Direct descent is recommended owing to loose stuff in separate pitches. Lifelining can be done with aid of old winch, but it is NOT SAFE to use as a winch. At bottom further 40 feet pitch to where small stream can be heard. From Grand Canyon continue along passage at head of Elizabeth Shaft to

Stalactite Passage. Hole in floor requires delicate traverse on left hand wall. Where large boulders are met is top of Crumble Pot, requiring 75 feet ladder. Get off ladder before reaching bottom and climb up slope to head of **Beza Shaft.** Alternatively ladder can be threaded across and down Beza shaft by first man down Crumble Pot. Beza Shaft can be belayed and laddered from top of Crumble Pot or from calcited boulders after 12 feet chimney down shaft. From here it is 160 feet ladder climb. At bottom turn left (facing ladder) and enter via very loose large rift into similarly loose large chamber. Passing over chamber enter tight crawl for 6 feet to head of last pitch, needing 50 feet rope. At bottom stream can again be heard.

Far Flats are entered by crawling along Flats at foot of entrance pitch away from Grand Canyon, and descending 35 feet pitch. Get off ladder a few feet from bottom and enter Boulder Passage, leading into Firbeck Hall. Scaling ladders are here needed to climb to Far Flats.

Tackle required :

		Ladder.	Belay.	Lifeline.
		ft.	ft.	ft.
Entrance Pitch	...	180	—	70 and 140
Second Pitch	...	35	—	50
(Grand Canyon)	...	Handline 50		
Elizabeth Shaft	...	180	30	200
Bottom of Elizabeth	...	40	20	50
Crumble Pot	...	75	20	100
Beza Pot	...	160	20	200
Bottom of Beza	...	Handline 50		

References : M. H. Chantry 1937, Caves and Caving, No. 1, pp. 34-37, **S.** Salmon and Boldock 1951, Cave Science, No. 16, pp. 331-8, **S.**

NETTLE CAVE

Deepdale.
See Deepdale Cave.

NETTLE SHAFT POT   See MOUNTBATTEN POT

NEW SPEEDWELL MINE   (Matlock Bath)
See SPEEDWELL MINE

NICKER GROVE MINE and CAVE   E.C.
    215761   See Map No. 9

Eyam.

Altitude 700ft. Length 300ft.

On west side of Cucklet Dale above overgrown mine heaps. Mined passage leads to two solution cavities, the larger some 60 feet long, 25 feet high and up to 10 feet wide.

ODIN CAVE   E.C.
    135834   See Map No. 1

Castleton.

Altitude 850ft. Length 140ft. Map No. 15.

West side of Mam Tor road close to Odin Mine. Nice cave entrance. Very muddy and one chamber. 40 feet shaft above leads into mud-filled continuation.

ODIN CAVERN   D.C.
    275529

Wirksworth.

Altitude 800ft.

First explored O.C.

In Sprink Wood, ¼ mile east of Pittywood Farm. Entrance 4 feet high.

Short passage leads to four large chambers filled with ochreous clay filling. Contains mine level.

Also known as FOXHOLES.

ODIN MINE

133834

See Map No. 1

Castleton.

Altitude 950ft.   Depth 450ft.   Length   Map No. 15

Approach from west side of Mam Tor road to top of impressive
fissure.   Tie hand line round tree on north side and descend into
first crack.   Along passage 25 feet chimney is climbed (here rope
is handy) and leads to second shaft and lower workings.   From
bottom of this shaft many loose boulders.   No natural caverns
and final pitches of 40 feet and 40 feet or one 60 feet in different sections of mine should be treated with great care.   Old
miner's pick axe found in mud banks at lowest level (S.P.C.C.
1948).

Tackle :

			Ladder.	Belay.	Lifeline.
			ft.	ft.	ft.
1st Pitch	...	...	80 handline	—	—
2nd Pitch	...	...	100 handline	—	—
3rd Pitch	...	...	40	30	60
4th Pitch	...	...	40	30	60
5th Pitch	...	..	60	30	80

OLD ASH MINE

M.C.

269605

Wensley.

Altitude 600ft.

An adit on the west side of Northern Dale, opposite Lords and Ladies
Mine.   Roughly midway between Wensley and Snitterton.   Adit
leads into a solution cave extensively altered by mining.

Reference : D. Nash 1957, Trans. Cave Research Group, Vol. V,
No. 1.

OLD BILL'S SWALLET

E.C. Dig

044716

See Map No. 4

Stanley Moor, Buxton.

Altitude 1,300ft.

Small cave 10 feet long at base of rock outcrop on Stanley Moor.
A small stream sinks among loose boulders in wet weather.   An
impenetrable crack to right also.

OLD BROOK CAVE   M.C.

172805

Bradwell.

See BRADWELL PARISH CAVE.

OLD CRESSBROOK CAVE   E.C.

173733

Cressbrook Area.

Altitude 660ft. Length 50ft.

Directly opposite Cressbrook Resurgence Cave is large cave entrance.
Large passage for 30 feet and then muddy crawl to small chamber.

OLD HANNAH'S HOLE   E.C.

100557   See Map No. 7

Manifold.

Altitude 800ft. Depth   Length 45ft. Map No. 18.

West side of Redhurst Gorge, south of Wetton Mill. Fissure entrance
10 feet high and narrowing.

Supposed natural explosions took place here and at DARFAR CRAG
CAVE. Human remains excavated 1896; in Hanley Museum,
Staffs.

References : T. Wardle 1899, Trans. N. Staffs. Field Club XXXIII,
pp. 97 and 105.   D. Bramwell 1950, Trans. Cave Research
Group, Vol. I, No. 4.

OLD TOR MINE   M.C.

134828   See Map No. 1

Winnats Pass, Castleton.

Also known as TRIANGLE CAVE.

Altitude 1,250ft. Length 300ft. Depth 70ft.

Adit entrance high on north side of Winnats at end of path. Short
adit leads into main chamber with shaft to surface at far end.
Pipe-vein workings for Blue John stone extend north-westwards
to muddy slope into lower passage. Muddy sump at end leads
only to short passage.

Beware infection from generations of cavers' litter and dead sheep.

OLD WOMAN'S CAVE   E.C. Arch.

165708

Taddington Dale.

Altitude 700ft. Depth 20ft. Length 44ft.

100 feet above road south side of Taddington Dale above crags. An easy climb down 15 feet into chamber, small passages lead off.

Difficult to find in broken ground and undergrowth.

Iron Age pottery in British Museum, London.

References : W. S. Fox 1911, Derbyshire Arch. Jour. XXXIII, p. 115. J. W. Brailsford 1959, Derbys. Arch. Jour., LXXVII, p. 56.

ONE ASH CAVE E.C.

172651 See Map No. 3

Lathkilldale.

Altitude 800ft. Length 100ft.

A small cave on shelf behind undergrowth in the western cliffs at the upper end of Calesdale ¼ mile east-south-east of ONE ASH GRANGE. Another small cave in cliff face a few yards to the north.

Often confused with UPPER CALESDALE CAVE which is at the same level a third of a mile to the north, above the Lower Calesdale Cave.

ORCHARD MINE CAVERNS Lost

Wirksworth.

No longer known—approximate site of mine is 283550 in one of many veins lying parallel to and on east of Middleton-Wirksworth road.

Reference: Farey 1811, p. 294, which appears to be confused with Orchard Pipe Caverns at Winster on p. 264.

OSSOM CRAG CAVE E.C.

095557 See Map No. 7

Manifold.

Altitude 700ft. Depth Length 60ft. Map No. 18

100 feet up on west side of Manifold, lower down valley than Wetton Mill. Rock shelter with upward fissure. Contains downwards hands and knees crawl widening slightly. Might be forced further.

References : D. Bramwell 1957, The Lyre, Vol. I (2), pp. 20-21 (Section of deposits). D. Bramwell 1955-6, P.A. N/L 11, 12, 13.

OSSOM'S EYRIE Arch.

095557 See Map No. 7

Manifold Valley.

Altitude 780ft.

References : D. Bramwell and S. Gee 1956, Peakland Arch. Soc.,
  N/L 13. D. Bramwell and S. Gee 1957, Peakland Arch. Soc.
  N/L 14. D. Bramwell and S. Gee 1958, Peakland Arch. Soc.
  N/L 15.

A small archaeological bone cave in the face of Ossom's crag. Noted
for bird remains.

OTTER HOLE RESURGENCE   V.D.C.

047733   See Map No. 4

Stanley Moor, Buxton.

Altitude 1,200ft. Length 120ft.

In field by Otter Hole Farm. Powerful resurgence. Dug by Eldon
Pothole Club 1962-3.

Crawl in stream for 35 feet to flake dividing passage. Pass on left,
then squeeze lying in water on side. Follow stream crawling in
water to duck, which can be passed and 5 feet on is crawl into
chamber with tin-bath jammed in hole in roof! Stream flows
out of silted up bedding plane and is known to come from Re-
surgence/Swallet 120 feet away, though ultimate source not known.
Digging still in progress.

Resurgence/Swallet for above   V.D.C.

Dug in 1963 in centre of Fairway on Cavendish Golf Course! Permission rarely granted. Keep out!

Stream runs across floor of shakehole. Possible to squeeze into
bedding in sink into passage 2½ feet high, half full of water.
Possible to crawl and swim for 120 feet when water is low.

Reference: Eldon Pothole Club Newsletter, Vol. V, No. 2. Vol. V, No.
10, S.

OWL HOLE

071683   See Map No. 5

Earlsterndale.

Reference : P. Smith 1959, The Lyre, Vol. I, No. 3, p. 67.

50 feet deep open pot with short crawl north-west. Easy scramble down
on south side.

OWLET HOLE   E.C.

198633

Middleton-by-Youlgreave.

A small cave in the dale leading down from the village. It is uncertain to which of several small joint and bedding caves this name should be applied. None have been penetrated for more than 10 feet or so, though digging might be repaid.

OWLET MINE

E.C.

292580

See Map No. 8

Matlock Bath.

Also known as VICTORIA CAVERN.

Altitude 500ft. Length 400ft.

Reference : C. N. Maddocks 1958, The Lyre, Vol. I, No. 3, pp. 42-3, S.

A mined pipe vein.

OXCLOSE MINE

D.P.

275597

See Map No. 8

Snitterton.

Altitude 730ft.

Usual entrance is " Escape route " shaft in field at rear of Leawood Cottage (headquarters of Operation Mole, from whom permission should be sought). First pitch of 60 feet with ladder belayed to rail to hang clear of ginging. Then short crawl to head of 2nd pitch (25 feet) with ladder belayed to foot of first. Separate lifeline possible, but climbers should not be on both pitches at the same time. From foot of second pitch proceed down dip along 700 feet crawl (more comfortable feet first but care not to go down 80 feet shaft at side). At end is mined area around engine shaft on 200 feet level from surface. By-pass this and continue down into ramifying workings and solution caves, passing a 10 feet pitch (with rotting rope of unknown vintage) and the phosphorescent pool (actually reflecting daylight from 200 feet above) into flooded chambers. Route finding difficult. On returning a passage to the south leads into the dangerous upper parts of recent mine workings from the now flooded 300 feet level. Otherwise route may be found from Engine Shaft by keeping up dip on a calcite floor.

References : D. Nash 1957, Trans. Cave Research Group, Vol. V, No. 1.

OXLOW CAVERNS

D.P.

126824

See Map No. 1

Castleton.

Altitude 1,400ft. Depth 450ft. Length over 1,000ft.

On hillside ¼ mile south of Oxlow House Farm. Entrance mine shaft covered by iron lid.

Entrance pitch 55 feet belayed to iron bar under lid. Bottom of the shaft is narrow and requires care. Continue down boulder slope in large chamber and turn left at bottom. Short crawl leads to head of Second Pitch, 40 feet. Belay to metal rings on right hand wall, with additional belay only on baulk of timber. Third Pitch, 45 feet, follows soon after, with belay rings in left-hand wall (facing chamber). This pitch is top of East Chamber and gives fine views if well lit up. Foot of pitch is crest with slopes leading in opposite directions to East and West Chambers. To East Chamber continue down slope and awkward rift climb (30 feet handline useful).

In bottom of chamber is short unstable pitch into abandoned dig, once thought to open into a passage to Nettle Pot. Return to crest of slopes at foot of Third Pitch and descend west slope, taking great care over and under deads supported only on stemples. On reaching large baulk of timber, this is head of Fourth Pitch, which can be done either with 80 feet ladder from timber or by 40 feet ladder with handline only down first steeply sloping part. Lifelining can be done either as one from the top or in two parts, the slope from the top, and the vertical from a "Sentry Box" at the head of the pitch. In either case great care is needed on going over the lip.

From the bottom continue down easy sloping passage into West Antechamber. Low stream passage on right ends in sump up-stream, possibly draining from New Upper Series of Giants Hole. Bearing left, large West Chamber is reached with remnants of ore-washing on floor and stemples high in roof. Short mined passage beyond leads to Waterfall Chamber, with entry from Maskhill Mine from roof above. Hole in newly collapsed floor has 35 feet pitch into Pearl Chamber with short 12 feet pitch into Final Sump at 450 feet depth.

Tackle required :

	Ladder.	Belay.	Lifeline.
	ft.	ft.	ft.
First Pitch	55	—	70
Second Pitch	40	15	50
Third Pitch	45	30	70
East Chamber ...	30 handline	—	—
Fourth Pitch	80	—	100
or	40	100	50 + 50
Fifth Pitch (wet) ...	40	20	60
(into Pearl Chamber)			
Sixth Pitch	12	10	—

Round trip made be made via Maskhill Mine (see under) by experienced persons.

Permission must be obtained from Oxlow House Farm.

Once known as Rickety Mine—Puttrell MSS.

Reference : Salmon and Boldock 1951, Cave Science, Vol. III, No. 17, pp. 13-30, **S.**

PARSLEY HAY CAVE   D.C.

037629

Parsley Hay.

Altitude 1,000ft. Length 20ft.

In Long Dale in small disused quarry south of Vincent House. Entrance high up in quarry. 12 feet crawl then very tight into small chamber. No way on. Only to be attempted by thin men.

PEAK CAVERN   Show D.C.

149825   See Map No. 1

Castleton.

Altitude 625ft. Length 2 miles. Map No. 15.

At foot of perpendicular cliff immediately behind Castleton. Entrance massive cave in which rope making is carried out, 330 feet x 102 feet x 6 feet high.

Halfway on left of cavern is 240 feet passage to Swine Hole. Visitors walk descends to Inner Styx, long shallow pool and then to Great Chamber, 150 feet x 90 feet x 40 feet. High boulder slope leads to roomy passage—Orchestra Chamber—and descends to Roger Rains House. From Pluto's Dining Room steep descent leads to stream in Halfway House. Stream can be followed for 120 feet to sump. Passage continues for 480 feet to the Junction where stream comes in on the left. This is Buxton Water. Right passage at Junction leads through Five Arches to Victoria Cavern, over 80 feet high, and then becomes a narrow passage with deep pools to Speedwell Water.

Former sump at end of Speedwell Water Passage has been partly drained and is now a muddy wallow, leading to long Upper Gallery with branches to the Treasury, Wind Tunnel, Pickering's Crawl, etc. Upper Gallery meets Main Stream Passage at 20 feet pitch—the Surprise View. Main Stream Passage is high and wide downstream to upper end of Buxton Water Sump (400 feet long). Upstream first main branch on right is up Squaw's Junction Waterfalls to several muddy passages with small grottos. Next on left is Lake Passage with 17 feet long sump, which has been passed to short flooded passage with high rift cavern above. Beyond is Ink Sump, explored by divers for over 300 feet into submerged parallel master cave. Up main stream passage beyond Lake Passage is climb up to Boulder Chamber. Steep scramble up to left leads to silted up passage which might connect with Ink Sump master cave. Main passage continues to Far Sump, which has been explored by divers for some 200 feet before getting too narrow.

References : J. C. Gilbert 1949, Cave Science, Vol. II, No. 10, S. E. Simpson 1948, Cave Science, Vol. I, No. 3, S. L. Salmon 1952, Cave Science, Vol. III, No. 20, S. L. Salmon 1962, Cave Science, Vol. IV, No. 31, S.

•

PEAK DALE CAVE   E.C.

090770

Peak Dale, near Buxton.

Altitude 1,000ft. Length 90ft.

South of road, opposite signal box, in quarry entrance which has been bridged over.

Low entrance into passage 5 feet high and 2½ feet wide, with 2 feet of water. Ended in fine grotto which has been largely destroyed in abortive attempts to push further. Water has been pumped out and a crack leads to a narrow pitch. The cave is below a waste lime tip and the lime in the water is mildly caustic. A calcite film soon forms on the water if left undisturbed.

PEAKSHILL CAVE, Castleton   See Giant's Cave

PERRYFOOT CAVE   D.C.

100812   See Map No. 1

Perryfoot, Castleton.

Altitude 1,026ft. Length 600ft.

Entrance in hollow immediately north of road, close to impenetrable stream sink. Obvious dry entrance to left of sink. After short crawl and walk, small chamber has choice of two ways on, which link up. At floor level tight crawl in passage with small pools leads to Iron Maiden squeeze, which is extremely tight and must not be attempted by large persons. Beyond Iron Maiden passage leads on to final chamber. Alternative route is by delicate climb (15 feet) out of main passage, followed by very tight crawl for 10 feet, then series of crawls and walking. Turn sharp left at bottom of very muddy slope. Stream can be heard at bottom of very narrow shaft but cannot be reached. Continue along muddy passage to final chamber with concrete dams. Baling by B.S.A. only resulted in a narrow passage with bad air. Crossing chamber to left leads to Iron Maiden.

Sump in final chamber is at 970 feet O.D. some 180 yards short of Coalpthole Rake and about 100 feet above the "Lost Swallet." Water reappears at Russet Well in Castleton.

References : L. Salmon and G. Boldock 1949, Cave Science, Vol. II, No. 9, **S**. L. Salmon and G. Boldock 1950, Cave Science, Vol. II, No. 11. L. Salmon 1963, Cave Science, Vol. V, No. 33, **S**.

PERSEVERANCE POT   M.P.

044714   See Map No. 4

Stanley Moor, Buxton.

Altitude 1,250ft. Length 120ft. Depth 90ft.

In 3rd Shakehole north of Stanley Moor Reservoir.

Dug by Eldon Pothole Club in 1962.

Six feet drop between boulders to 20 feet slope, then further 6 feet drop into passage at right angles. Turn left and cross two holes in floor (care—40 feet deep). Continue to hole on left which is 25 feet pitch. Belay to Rawl Bolt. Pitch tight and ends on muddy slope of 15 feet. Then short iron ladder to short muddy passage and three muddy chambers. Digging in progress.

Tackle : 25ft. ladder, 40ft. lifeline.

Reference: Eldon Pothole Club Newsletter, Vol. V, No. 4, and No. 10, **S**.

PEVERIL CASTLE CAVE

150826   See Map No. 1

Castleton.

See Cavedale Caves.

PICKERING TOR CAVE   E.C.

143531   See Map No 6

Dovedale.

Altitude 550ft. Map No. 17.

Opposite Ilam Rock, 100 feet up Pickering Dale. Small Cave.

PIKERS PIT   Dig

068685   See Map No. 5

Earlsterndale.

Altitude 1,225ft.

525 feet west of Greensides Farm.

Large collapsed swallet. Boulder ruckle penetrable for only a few feet. Water resurges at Dowel Resurgence.

Reference : P. Smith 1959, The Lyre, Vol. I, No. 3, p. 62.

PINHOLE CAVE   E.C.

532741

Cresswell.

Altitude 300ft. Length 80ft.

At west end of Cresswell Crags.

Furnished most complete record of human and animal occupation of any British Caves. Finds can be seen in Derby Museum; Manchester University Museum; British Museum, London; Middlesborough Museum.

PIPPINS HOLE

Hazlebadge, Bradwell.

Probably that now known as Quarter's Farm Swallet.

Reference : Farey 1811, p. 296.

THE PIT HOLE   M.C.

098664   See Map No. 5

Earlsterndale.

Altitude 1,000ft.

Choked tube in south corner of quarry. Grating in road nearby covers natural fissure.

Reference : P. Smith 1959, The Lyre, Vol. I, No. 3, p. 60.

PLACKET MINE CAVERN

Winster.

Farey 1811, p. 294. 1st Lime. 120 yards high.

A " lost " cavern—there are two Plackett Mines at 239608 and 232611. Various small caverns have been found by Op. Mole but none 120 yards high.

PLUNGE HOLE   M.P.

044713   See Map No. 4

Buxton.

Altitude 1,220ft. Depth 50ft. Length 30ft.

Situated in second shakehole from north wall of Stanley Moor reservoir where stream runs into Boulders.

Crawl under large boulder into a small chamber with large boulder apparently blocking way on. Route is under this (care) into 40 feet deep rift (rope or ladder useful) which it is possible to climb down. Stream at bottom. Downstream after 20 feet, too narrow. Upstream for 10 feet to boulders through which stream enters. Low crawl leads to small chamber, then tight squeeze into 5 feet deep hole with choked bedding plane.

Water thought to reappear in Poole's Cavern.

Tackle : 50ft. rope or ladder but no safe belay so lifelining highly desirable.

Reference : British Caver 1950, Vol. XX, p. 83.

POOLES CAVERN   Show
050726   See Map No. 4

Buxton.

Altitude 1,100ft. Length 1,800ft.

In south portion of Buxton (Green Lane).

Archaeological show cave, Romano-British animal remains excavated being on show in museum attached. Contains Roman Chamber, Font and natural arch with stalactite shaped like flitch of bacon. One of the chambers is 100 feet high.

Illuminated by gas.

After leaving public section it is possible to crawl upstream to a boulder choke. Also above fence are two chambers at top of boulder scree. Roots from surface can be seen in upper chamber. Water sinks in Swallow holes on Stanley Moor, notable Plunge Hole, and rises again at Wye Head.

Stalagmites have grown 3 inches on gas pipes.
References : W. B. Dawkins 1874, " Cave Hunting," p. 126. E. A. Glennie 1953-4, Cave Research Group Newsletter, 45 and 48.

POUNDER CAVE   E.C.
280588   See Map No. 8

Bonsall.

Altitude 870ft. Length about 100ft.

In end of crags east of Pounder Lane. Small arched entrance with remains of wall across. Easy passage trending downwards, partly dug out at bottom. Might be of archaeological interest both on threshold and in gritstone gravel near bottom which suggests it was a former swallet.

Nearby mine level has a dangerously unstable roof and is best avoided.

QUARTERS FARM SWALLET   D.C.

173795   See Map No. 2

Altitude 750ft.

Bradwell.

Sink in trees some 200 yards north of farm. Has been dug out but
has become choked with flood debris again. Only short tight
passage reached.

Listed by Farey as Hazlebadge Swallow. May also have been known
as Pippins Hole.

RAINS CAVE   E.C./Arch.

226553

Brassington.

Altitude 1,100ft. Length 30ft.

Entrance concealed behind large boulders at east of Longcliffe crags,
about 100 yards west of Observer Corps Box.

Sloping chamber with crawls off. Incompletely excavated. Numerous
animal remains and some prehistoric pottery found.

Also known as Longcliffe Fissure.

References : J. Ward 1889, Derbys. Arch. Jour., Vol. XI, p. 31 (plan).
J. Ward 1892, Derbys. Arch. Jour., Vol. XIV, p. 228 (section).
J. Ward 1893, Derbys. Arch. Jour., Vol. XV, p. 161.

RANTER MINE CAVERN

Wirksworth.

A "lost" cavern listed by Farey (1811). Probably in the vein running parallel to and east of the Middleton to Wirksworth road.
Ranter Mine shaft is about 284550. Orchard Mine Cavern is
probably close by.

RAVEN MINE   M.P.

158660   See Map No. 3

Monyash.

Altitude 880ft. Depth 100ft.

Old lead mine shaft west of Fern Dale branch of Lathkill Dale.
Shaft 100 feet deep but last 50 feet is in natural pot. Leads
to large clay-filled bedding plane.

RAVENSCLIFFE CAVE   E.C. Arch.

174735

Cressbrook.

Altitude 1,000ft.

In cliffs high on east side of dale. West of Hay Top. Single large chamber with crawl at back. Archaeologically excavated.

References : W. S. Fox 1910, Derbys. Arch. Jour., Vol. XXXII, p. 141.

J. W. Brailsford 1959, Derbys. Arch. Jour., Vol. LXXVII, pp. 55-6. Has been confused with Bull Tor Cave in next crag to south.

REDHURST SWALLET   D.C.

098558   See Map No. 7

Manifold Valley.

Altitude 610f⁺. Length 1,000ft.

South side of river ¼ mile upstream from Redhurst Bridge. Long crawl at bottom of entrance pitch in dry conditions. Side passage is in rift with crawl at bottom. Deep pool leads to rift with undulating floor. Sump passed in 1959 drought and extensive rift passages entered.

Whole cave liable to flood with onset of rain. One hour's respite only.

Unpublished Survey by Orpheus C.C.

REYNARDS CAVE   E.C.

148525   See Map No. 6

Dovedale.

Altitude 360ft. Length 40ft.

A natural arch and cave high on the east side of Dovedale. Between Bostern Grange and Sharplow Dale.

Two small caves behind arch. Larger is Reynards Cave, the other Reynard's Kitchen, with small climb in roof.
Archaeologically excavated.

RICKLOW CAVE   D.C.

163661   See Map No. 3

Lathkill Dale.

Altitude 700ft. Depth 20ft. Length 250ft.

Small fissure entrance enlarged by mining in the dale bottom immediately below Ricklow Marble Quarry tip. Short passage leads to 15 feet pitch (climbable but rope useful for return) into small chamber with two crawls leading off. Right hand crawl leads through water to 12 feet pitch into small pot. Three passages enter in roof but all close after a short distance. Other crawl at foot of 15 feet pitch is very muddy and leads to 60 feet long tube ending in a choke, which is worth digging, but tube has to be reversed with each load of debris !

The name, Ricklow Cavern, has been applied to Lathkill Head Cave in the past, but this is now considered to be ill-advised and should be forgotten.

The quarry above has a partly collapsed choked cave entrance at the extreme east which might be worth digging, as well as underground marble mines now in a dangerously unstable condition.

ROBIN HOOD CAVE   Arch.
535742

Creswell.

Altitude 300ft.

In Creswell Crags, $\frac{1}{4}$ mile east of village.

Archaeological finds in British Museum, and Manchester Museum.
Reference : Geological Survey Memoirs on N. Part of Derbyshire Coalfield 1913, pp. 106-7, S.

ROBIN HOOD'S CAVE   E.C.
243837

Stanage Edge, Hathersage.

Altitude 1,350ft.   Length 50ft.

A series of wind-eroded holes in the gritstone scarp.   Used by climbers for camping.

ROMAN CAVES   Show
298589
See Map No. 8
Matlock Bath.

A partly open old lead mine fissure connecting with Fern Cave, on the summit of High Tor.

ROWTER HOLE   V.D.P.
133823
See Map No. 1
Castleton.

Altitude 1,450ft.   Depth 320ft.

800 feet north-east of Rowter Farm, south of the Winnats.   Mine shaft through solid rock for 240 feet.   Last part through chamber 60 feet high, 20 feet wide and 150 feet long.   At west end descend through boulder choke into passage to Abyss, now blocked. At upper end is hanging scree slope, up wall and 20 feet chimney

to Upper Chamber. Second shaft at east end is safer (50 feet deep) Spar chamber negotiated by back and knee traverse over boulders to shaft and sump.

Also known as Rowter Pot and once called Longcliff Caverns.

Reference : J. Randles 1933, The Speleologist, No. 1, S.

ROYAL MINE   (Matlock Bath)   See SPEEDWELL MINE

RUGS HALL.   *Alternate name for top level of*
BALL EYE MINE

RUTLAND CAVERN   Show

293585   See Map No. 8

Matlock Bath.

Altitude 675ft.   Length 560ft.

Formerly known as Old Nestus Grotto.

On Heights of Abraham, approached through grounds off Upperwood Road. Artificial passage for 240 feet leads to chamber 300 feet long. Branches into two near end. On left is Old Nestus Cavern, one of oldest lead mines in Derbyshire with good evidence of pick work. Good mineralisation features, in upper galleries up Roman Stairs. Also various rare minerals found in Lower Nestus workings down shaft (now blocked) below Tower House.

RUSSET WELL

148827   See Map No. 1

Castleton.

Altitude 625ft.

Main resurgence for Castleton area, in private garden on east side of entrance to Peak Cavern Gorge. Water rises from hole in a mineral vein some 10 feet below the surface of a pool. Pumping into water mains during droughts has failed to lower the level more than an inch or so.

RYAN and SOMERVILLES QUARRY CAVES

080693

Hindlow, Buxton.

Altitude about 1,250ft.

In Hindlow Quarry, north-west of station. High in quarry face.

Several sections of the same cave have been broken into, and quarried away at intervals from 1956. A profusion of bones of lion, horse, bison, etc., was discovered, also a pot with a good stalagmite flow. Eldon Pothole Club records.

ST. BERTRAM'S CAVE   E.C.

106540   See Map No. 8

Manifold Valley.

Altitude 650ft. Length 600ft.

Near Beeston Tor Farm. Entrance formerly had door. Another entrance is window high in cliff. Mostly muddy crawls. Several small chambers, with possible continuation below the Cellars.

Archaeological remains in British Museum and Buxton Museum. Hoard of Saxon coins found here.

References : G. H. Wilson 1926, Some Crags and Caves of Peakland, p. 38. G. H. Wilson 1934, Cave Hunting Holidays in Peakland, p. 47.

SALLET HOLE CAVE   D.C.

223743

Stoney Middleton.

Altitude 900ft. Length 75ft.

High in west side of gully off south side of Coombs Dale. Entrance chamber leads to left passage with 15 feet pot in floor, and right passage (partly mined) with 200 feet deep shaft in floor—danger ! This shaft goes straight through roof of Sallet Hole Mine now being reopened.

THE SALTPAN

216763

Eyam.

Altitude 730ft.

Not really a cave, but a narrow gorge at the north end of Cucklet Dell. Reputed to have had a roof over it once.

SAND HOLES SWALLET   Dig

071675   See Map No. 5

Earlsterndale.

Altitude 1,200ft.

1,000 yards west of Dowell Farm under north face of Chrome Hill. A dig in a choked swallet. Water reappears at Dowell Resurgence.

Reference : P. Smith 1960, The Lyre, Vol. I, No. 3, p. 63.

SEVEN WAYS CAVE

098548

Arch.

See Map No. 7

Manifold Valley.

On back of hill containing Thor's Cave, and close to Elderbush Cave. Short series of passages with seven branches or entrances.

References : D. Bramwell 1952, Peakland Arch. Soc. Newsletter, 8. D. Bramwell 1954, Peakland Arch. Soc. Newsletter, 10.

SHAY LODGE SINKS

038729

Digs ?

See Map No. 4

Buxton.

Altitude 1,200ft.

Ths area around Shay Lodge Farm above Burbage, Buxton, has several sinks and shakeholes whose waters could resurge at either Otter Hole or Wye Head. One cave can be entered by crawling for 20 feet. Digging in progress.

Reference : Eldon Pothole Club Newsletters, Vol. V, No. 4.

SHEEPWASH CAVE

100813

D.C.

See Map No. 1

Perryfoot, Castleton.

Altitude 1,100ft. Length 200ft.

Also known as Manifold Cave, though this name has also been applied to Perryfoot Cave and to Gautries Hole, with resulting confusion !

In hollow 200 feet north-west of road junction at Perryfoot. Inconspicuous narrow fissure entrance, which takes a stream, partly from a culvert. Passages all crawling and tight. Some 40 feet in passage divides. Left fork leads into chamber after tight crawl. Ends 100 feet on with pool which ebbs and flows. Right fork leads to Letter Box, a low slit, and to steep clay banks, pools and loose boulders. Close by are two other caves, one a tight crawl for 15 feet only; the other is a crawl for 60 feet with a 15 feet pitch.

Perryfoot Stream was diverted into Sheepwash Cave during the working of Coalpithole Mine.

References : L. Salmon and G. Boldock 1950, Cave Science, Vol. II, No. 11, S. L. Salmon 1963, Cave Science, Vol. V, No. 33, p. 36, S.

SLINTER WOOD CAVES

See Map No. 8

M.C.

288571

Cromford.

Altitude 550ft.

Three small caves in the cliff almost opposite Ball Eye Mine. The Floor of one has recently collapsed revealing a 100 feet deep hole.

SNELSLOW SWALLET

Dig

114823

See Map No. 1

Castleton.

Altitude 1,120ft. Length 55ft.

A series of parallel fissures ¼ mile south-west of Giant's Hole. Stream has entered all of fissures at one time or another, and has been diverted back and forth during abortive digs. All the fissures become too tight—6 inches wide and 15-20 feet high. Water can be heard falling inside. Good possibilities if entry can be forced.

Reference : Salmon and Boldock 1950, Cave Science, Vol. II, No. 11.

S — P HOLE (Perryfoot)   See COCKSHEAD MINE

SPEEDWELL MINE and CAVERN

Mine

292579

See Map No. 8

Matlock Bath.

Altitude 550ft.

Old lead mine formerly a show cave with adit entrance now partly concealed by rubbish in road fork at Upperwood. Parts more recently worked for fluorspar and calcite via adits, as Royal Mine from top of Old Pavilion Grounds, and accessible by adits from there. Also known as New Speedwell Mine, and once as Angelina's Cavern, though that name more strictly applied to a chamber now mined away.

Whole system is somewhat unstable, and parts are in a dangerous state. Through route to Fluorspar Cavern at one time, now blocked.

SPEEDWELL MINE and CAVERN   Show and V.D.C.

139828

See Map No. 1

Castleton.

Altitude 810ft. Length about 2½ miles.

Entrance to show cave at foot of Winnats Pass, by flight of steps down to Grand Canal. Visitors taken by boat along to Bottomless Pit at about 500 yards south from entrance. Bottomless Pit lake is 70 feet below and has been dived without success. Water reappears at Russet Well in Castleton some 40 feet lower and ¼ mile away. Above Bottomless Pit is high cavern in Foresides Rake (referred to by Farey as Devil's Hall). Old workings believed to extend to surface some 600 feet above. Canal continues into Stream Passage upstream to Main Rising (½ mile) which is 70 feet deep. Branches nearby to Cliff Cavern (200 feet high) and Bathing Pool (with lake 50 feet deep).

To reach these Whirlpool must be crossed by swimming or rubber dinghy. Whirlpool Passage on right is 1,100 feet long, ending in old workings with Ebbing and Flowing Spring in floor. Overflow water goes down Bung Hole (walled dam in stream passage with 18 feet iron ladder in waterfall). Half mile down stream to sump (on same level as Speedwell Pot in Peak Cavern and Russet Well). Passage goes under old pipe workings and close by a dry ox-bow by-passes the very low bedding cave on the stream passage.

At far end of Rift Cavern is Puttrell's Pool with concealed near duck on left leading on. Branch on left leads back to near Bung Hole. Sandy branch on right leads to sand chokes.

Crawl on right from Far Canal leads to Assault Course series with single 50 feet high chamber believed to be part of Pilkington's lost cavern of 1789.

References : J. W. Puttrell 1937-8, Caves and Caving, Nos. 2, 3 and 4, S. T. D. Ford 1956, Trans. Cave Research Group, Vol. IV, No. 2, S. E. Simpson 1954, Cave Science, Col. III, No. 22, S. G. T. Warwick 1947, British Caver, Vol. XVII (on Pilkington's Cavern).

STANLEY MOOR CAVE   E.C.

047716   See Map No. 4

Buxton.

Altitude 1,220ft. Length 70ft.

In large shakehole on Stanley Moor. Discovered Eldon Pothole Club 1958.

Slope of 10 feet into entrance chamber. Tight passage on left slopes down into two small chambers with boulder chokes. 6 feet hole on right of entrance chamber leads into fine grotto with curtains and straw stalactites. Further sloping passage for 20 feet to choke. Digging in progress.

Gated: Apply Eldon Pothole Club.

Reference: Eldon Pothole Club Newsletter, Vol. 5, No. 10, S.

STONEY LOW SWALLET and HOLE   Dig?

069682   See Map No. 5

Earlsterndale.

Altitude 1,275ft.

Dye put in swallet took 44 hours to reach Dowel Resurgence, only 1,000 yards away and 325 feet lower.

Hole is at 070679 a little south of swallet at 1,325 feet altitude. Fissure in scarp leads to tight 50 feet pitch. Constricted dig possible at bottom.

Reference: P. Smith 1960, The Lyre, Vol. I, No. 13.

STOOP EDGE HOLE   D.P.

061685   See Map No. 5

Earlsterndale.

Altitude 1,425ft.

A tight fissure dug in 1957. 50 feet deep. No ladder required.
Reference: P. Smith 1960, The Lyre, Vol. I, No. 3.

SUICIDE CAVE   D.C.

139828   See Map No. 1

Altitude 825ft. Length 300ft.

On right near foot of Winnats Pass. Obvious entrance with second smaller one to left. First chamber has boulder slope with deceptive 15 feet drop at end. Route one is under start of slope. Left fork in second chamber leads to muddy crawls. Right to high third chamber. Back and foot traverse upwards at end leads to rising passage with boulder choke at end, a very promising dig, if means can be found to avoid collapse on diggers!

Also known as Horseshoe Cave.

SWALLOWDALE SINK   M.C.

063680   See Map No. 5

Earlsterndale.

Altitude 1,150ft.

Below Stoop Farm a slit entrance leads to choked bedding plane. Water can be heard below, and resurges a few hundred feet to west.

Reference: P. Smith 1960, The Lyre, Vol. I, No. 3.

SWALLOW TOR CAVE   Arch.

065678   See Map No. 5

Earlsterndale.

Altitude 1,000ft.

A small cave, excavated archaeologically.
Reference : P. Smith 1960, The Lyre, Vol. I, No. 3.

SWALLOW HOLES   Lost

An unknown cave near Buxton referred to by J. C. Cox in " The
    Tourists Guide to Derbyshire," p. 43.

SWEVIC HOUSE SWALLET   Dig

187775   See Map No. 9

Foolow.

Altitude 975ft.   Length 600ft.

In the northerly of two shakeholes in south-east corner of field 230
    yards west of Swevic House Farm.

Dig now extends about 200 feet to the west in 3 feet high stream
    passage, but entrance is liable to be blocked by rubbish.

Permission to visit rarely granted.

TADDINGTON DALE GROTTO   Lost

Taddington.

A grotto of which several photographs and vague articles appeared
    in the press about 1936 following the construction of the Tad-
    dington by-pass. Exact location unknown though the entrance is
    believed to lie in one of the by-pass cuttings now grassed over.

TEARSALL MINE   M.C.

262602

Wensley.

Altitude 950ft.

High on slopes south of Wensley village, above top of Northern Dale.

A series of mineralised flats and pipe veins intersecting solution caves.
    At present being worked opencast and access liable to be dangerous
    from loose stuff.

THIRST HOUSE CAVE

M.C. Arch.

097713

Deepdale, Kingsterndale.

Altitude 890ft. Length 190ft.

On east side of dale, well above dry bed, obvious entrance 15 feet high and 20 feet wide. Height soon drops to 6 feet and after 72 feet floor descends to second chamber. Hole in floor amongst boulders descends to short crawl and rift with pool below. Both chambers archaeologically excavated.

150 feet down dale is "Pool Cave" a short flooded mine working which has been dived and pumped dry !

Opposite Thirst House is Deepdale Cave—a long crawl. Thirst House has often been called Deepdale Cave incorrectly.

References : J. C. Cox 1890-1, Derbys. Arch. Jour., Vols. XII and XIII. J. Ward 1894-5, Derbys. Arch. Jour., Vols. XVI and XVII. W. Turner 1899, Ancient Remains near Buxton.

TACKO or TATCHO HOLE (Stoney Middleton)
See BOSSEN HOLE

THISTLE POT

E.P.

128812

See Map No. 1

Castleton.

Altitude 1,430ft.

On moor between Eldon Hole and top of Conies Dale. A water worn shaft being dug out by Pegasus. Now 55 feet deep with 30 feet fixed ladder. Rest easily climbable.

THOR'S CAVE

E.C.

098549

See Map No. 7

Manifold Valley.

Altitude 870ft. Length 150ft.

Very obvious entrance in prominent crag south-west of Wetton. Large chamber archaeologically excavated. Daylight penetrates most of it from "West Window."

Once known as Thyrsis's Cavern.

References : E. Brown 1865, Trans. Midland Scientific Assn., pp. 1, 19 and 70. S. Carrington 1866, The Reliquary, Vol. VI, p. 201. W. B. Dawkins 1874, Cave Hunting, p. 127. Heath 1882, Derbys. Arch. Jour., p. 165.

THOR'S FISSURE CAVERN

M.C.

099550

See Map No. 7

Manifold Valley.

Altitude 850ft.   Length 60ft.

Below and to south of Thor's Cave West Window.

A fissure cave which has been archaeologically excavated.

References : G. H. Wilson 1934, Cave Hunting Holidays in Peakland, p. 13. G. H. Wilson 1937, Caves and Caving, No. 2, p. 61, **S.** D. Bramwell 1950, Trans. Cave Research Group, Vol. I, No. 4.

TRACTOR POT

048707

Stanley Moor, Buxton.

Hole which appeared under a tractor, now refilled for safety. No prospect of extension.

TREAK CLIFF CAVERN

Show

136832

See Map No. 1

Castleton.

Altitude 950ft.   Length 1,000ft.

One mile west of Castleton on Mam Tor road, entrance by footpath up Treak Cliff.

An outer series of caves much altered by mining for Blue John stone, with good examples easily seen. An inner series of grottos with some of best stalactites in Derbyshire, discovered in 1926. Electric lighting throughout.

Also known as Tray Cliff Cave and as The Wonder Caves.

References : T. D. Ford 1954, Trans. Cave Research Group, Vol II, No. 2, **S.** J. Royse 1945, Ancient Castleton Caves, **S.**

TREAK CLIFF SEPULCHRAL CAVE

Immediately above Treak Cliff Cavern but now quarried away. Contained Bronze Age burial.

References : A. L. Armstrong 1923, Jour. Royal Anthropological Soc., Vol. LIII.

TREE HOLE

M.C.

135832

See Map No. 1

Castleton.

Altitude 1,000ft.   Length 300ft.

On Treak Cliff, to the north-west of the Show Cave and immediately
north of the old quarries. Shaft in hollow close to lone tree.
Easy 30 feet shaft (ladder and belay beam required) leads north
via fissure at foot (often choked with rubbish) and through muddy
crawls under stacked deads to two chambers with miners' debris.
A large collapsed choke forms the west (uphill) wall of the larger
chamber, and on the surface above a hollow suggests a former
continuation to both the larger rock-shelter visible from the valley, and to the small **Dielasma Cave** (named from a fossil abund-
ant in the adjacent rocks) close to the crest of the ridge. Some
50 feet long, this has been enlarged by mining and is easily
explored by stooping.

TRIANGLE CAVE   See OLD TOR MINE

TURNCLIFF SWALLET   E.C.

047700   See Map No. 4

Stanley Moor, Buxton.

Altitude 1,330ft. Length 10ft.

Near Turncliff Farm, where stream comes from under embank-
ment and sinks among boulders. Now diverted to sink 10 yards
away to right. 6 feet drop between boulders into bedding cave
blocked by boulder. Digging in progress, by Eldon Pothole Club.

VICTORIA CAVERN (Matlock Bath)
See OWLET MINE

VICTORY QUARRY FISSURE   Lost

0777

Doveholes.

A unique fissure cave containing Pliocene (pre Ice Age) mammal
remains. Now quarried away. Others may be waiting for dis-
covery.

Reference : W. B. Dawkins 1903, Quar. Jour. Geol. Soc., Vol. LIX,
pp. 105-129.

VIRGIN POT   S.P.

044715   See Map No. 4

Stanley Moor, Buxton.

Altitude 1,250ft. Depth 45ft.

In 4th shakehole north of Stanley Moor reservoir. Dug in 1962 by Eldon Pothole Club.

A short drop between boulders to tight oval hole in floor for 25 feet followed by 20 feet drop. Then too narrow.

Should only be attempted by small agile cavers.

Tackle : 25ft. ladder, 50ft. lifeline.

Reference: Eldon Pothole Club Newsletter, Vol. 5, No. 10, S.

WAKEBRIDGE CAVERN   Lost
339558

Crich.

A large cavern struck in the workings of the Wakebridge Mine, and once drained by a sough. Now inaccessible and possibly flooded.

Believed to be approximately 500 feet north of main engine shaft.

WALKER'S GROTTO   (Bradwell Dale)
See BRADWELL DALE CAVE

WAPPING MINE   Mine
294585   See Map No. 8

Matlock Bath.

Altitude 400ft.

A series of Pipe Vein workings connecting with Cumberland Cavern. Intermittently working, and dangerously unstable in older parts.

WATERFALL HOLE   S.S.P.
199770   See Map No. 9

Near Foolow.

Altitude 870ft.   Length 200ft.   Depth 150ft.

A large open pothole with a stream falling into it and trees all round. Easy scramble down on east side. Stream sinks into debris on floor but in flood overflows into bedding plane to north-east. This was opened in 1959 by Eldon Pothole Club after clearing debris. Extremely tight bedding crawl for 30 feet, which narrows until hole in floor is reached, 6 feet deep. Descend head first and enter small passage at bottom, very tight for 15 feet. Ward-Wins Crawl forward into small chamber, then slide down boulders to ledge (with care). This is top of Hockenhull's Rift, 35 feet deep (ladder required). Belay in small chamber above, stream appears at bottom of rift but do not follow. Descend at south-west end of rift between boulders for 15 feet followed by 12 feet drop. A further drop of 15 feet meets stream again. Chamber can be reached by climbing through boulders, and it contains muddy stalactites and small waterfall. Shaft can be descended for 20 feet at end of Showerbath passage in dry weather but is a dead end.

No accurate description of cave below Rift can be given as it is in a maze of large boulders.

Rescue of an injured man would be almost impossible through tight entrance passages. Take CARE.

Reference : B. King 1962, Cave Science, Vol. IV, No. 32, **S.**

LITTLE WATERFALL SWALLET

Lies 150 yards away to the north-east and is a possible dig.

WATERHOUSES FISSURE

0950

Waterhouses, Staffs.

Altitude 700ft.

Probably alternative name for Bank End Quarry Fissure, but may have referred to Lea House Quarry Cave.

References : E. Brown 1865, Trans. Midland Scientific Assn., p. 34. Heath 1882, Derbys. Arch. Jour., p. 164.

WATERLOW CAVERNS (Brassington)
See MANYSTONES QUARRY CAVES

WATERWAYS SWALLET   D.C.

126492

Swinscoe, Staffs.

Altitude 920ft.   Length 300ft.   Depth 120ft.

Entrance in valley 60 yards down from present sink. Rapid descent through boulder ruckle to steep bedding cave, and boulder chamber 130 feet from entrance. Large passage and 30 feet pitch (ladder required) to Final chamber and short low passage, terminating under large shakehole. The stream is not seen in the cave.

Reference : D. Mayer 1962, British Caver, Vol. XXXVI, p. 48.
Also called Waterings Swallet.

WETTON MILL HILL CAVE   M.C.

102562   See Map No. 7

Manifold Valley.

Altitude 900ft.

In crag at top of west side of Wetton Hill near two isolated thorn trees. Short muddy fissure passage.

WETTON MILL SINK   Dig ?

097561   See Map No. 7

Manifold Valley.

Altitude 600ft.

Entrance 500 feet below Wetton Bridge, by bend in river. Two sinks of which more northerly has only opened recently and water can be heard falling down a pitch.

WHALLEY CAVE   Arch.

511721

Cresswell.

An archaeological cave excavated by A. L. Armstrong. Nearby are some rock shelters.

WINDY KNOLL CAVE   E.C.

126830   See Map No. 1

Altitude 1,344ft. Length 120ft.

Castleton.

In field between Chapel and Sparrowpit roads west of Mam Tor. Broad low entrance in old quarry leads to large cavern. Crawl at end on right leads to second chamber. Low crawl to third chamber and impenetrable fissure.

Windy Knoll Fissure, which produced many thousands of animal bones is now obliterated and is believed to have been back-filled immediately outside present entrance. Remains in British Museum, Buxton, Manchester, Derby and Cambridge.

References : R. Pennington and W. B. Dawkins 1875, Quar. Jour. Geol. Soc., Vol. XXXI. W. B. Dawkins 1874, Cave Hunting, pp. 34 and 284. W. B. Dawkins 1877, Quar. Jour. Geol. Soc., Vol. XXXIII, p. 724.

WINNATS HEAD CAVE

E.C. Dig ?

See Map No. 1

131828

Castleton.

Altitude 1,300ft. Length 20ft.
In old quarry on south side of top of pass. Collapsed cave with roof
blocks resting on earth fill.

WINNATS CAVE

E.C.

See Map No. 1

135827

Castleton.

Altitude 1,150ft. Length 25ft.

Obvious round hole in buttress to the north-west of the bed in the
Winnats Pass. Short descent to single chamber some 10 feet in
diameter, with low muddy crawl on left.

WYE HEAD RESURGENCE

See Map No. 4

050731

Buxton.

Altitude 1,000ft.

On north side of Macclesfield road. The River Wye appears from
several places among rocks and includes water seen in Poole's
Cavern. Eldon Pothole Club penetrated 15 feet by clearing
boulders but were stopped by unstable roof under the road !
Now blocked again.

Reference: Eldon Pothole Club Newsletter, Vol. 5, No. 10.

YEW TREE CAVE

Arch.

516649

Pleasey Vale, Notts.

References : Ransom 1866, Report of the British Assn.   W. B.
Dawkins 1869, Quar. Jour. Geol. Soc.

Caving Clubs and their Secretaries

Birmingham Cave and Crag Club :
> D. Snell, 154 Station Road, Wylde Green, Sutton Coldfield, Warwickshire.

British Speleological Association (North Midlands Group) :
> J. Clark, 6 Twentywell View, Dore, Sheffield.

Crewe Cave and Pothole Club :
> Miss A. Keith, 9 Birch Grove, Rusholme, Manchester 14.

Derbyshire Caving Club :
> T. Davies, 1 Ash Grove, Marple, Stockport.

Derbyshire Pennine Club :
> 442 Glossop Road, Sheffield, 10.

Eccles Caving Club :
> B. Saville, 8 Park Drive, Monton, Eccles, Manchester.

Eldon Pothole Club :
> C. Ineson, 22 Heather Grove, Hollingworth, Hyde, Cheshire.

Fourways Club :
> R. J. A. Travis, 4 Elizabeth Grove, Gedling, Nottingham.

Hades Caving Club :
> J. Weil, 54 Ennerdale Road, Middleton, near Manchester.

Hyperion Club :
> D. Worth, 40 Gathurst Street, Manchester 18.

Leicester University Speleological Society :
> c/o Students' Union, The University, Leicester.

Macclesfield Caving Club :
> D. Whyte, Nescar Street, Macclesfield.

Manchester University Caving Society :
> c/o Students' Union, Oxford Road, Manchester.

Mansfield Pothole Club :
> C. C. Myles, 212 Chesterfield Road N., Mansfield, Notts.

Nottingham Caving Club :
> A. Harrison, 51 Brookhill Street, Stapleford, Notts.

Nottingham University Caving Club :
> c/o Students' Union, University, Nottingham.

Operation Mole :
> D. A. Nash, Hawthorne Villas, 39, Monk Street, Tutbury, Staffs.

Orpheus Caving Club :
> N. Pridmore, 29 Coral Street, Leicester.

Peak District Mines Historical Society:
      Mrs. P. Lunn, 28 Kenbourne Road, Nether Edge, Sheffield.

Peakland Archaeological Society:
      N. Davenport, 2 Avondale Road, Edgeley, Stockport.

Peverill Underground Survey Association:
      R. Taylor, 45 Spinkfield Road, Biskley, Huddersfield.

Pegasus Club:
      P. Watkinson, 11 Groville Drive, Woodthorpe.
      Nottingham.

Sale Caving Club:
      J. Curphey, 27 Keswick Road, Timperley, near Manchester.

Sheffield University Speleological Society:
      University House, Western Bank, Sheffield.

Sheffield Caving Club:
      C. Birley, Buchanan Crescent, Sheffield.

Shropshire Mining Club:
      D. R. Adam, Beech Mount, Station Road, Newport,
      Shropshire.

Swallownest Senior Scouts:
      R. Greaves, 83 Station Road, Woodhouse, Sheffield.

Glossary

ADIT. Level or sloping entrance to a mine, sometimes used for drainage.

ANASTOMOSIS. Random distribution of tubular channels of various sizes in bedding planes; also called spongework.

ARAGONITE. An unusual crystalline form of calcium carbonate.

AVEN. A vertical extension up from a passage, not breaking through to the surface, but sometimes leading to passages at higher levels.

BEDDING PLANE. The parting between two beds of rock, often enlarged to give a wide low cave penetrable by flat-out crawling.

BELAY. Point used for anchoring a ladder or rope, or a lifeline operator. TO BELAY—to attach the rope or ladder. BELAY ROPE—a short length used for anchoring.

BOULDER CHOKE. A mass of boulders blocking progress in a passage.

CALCITE. The commonest crystalline form of calcium carbonate; the chief constituent of limestone and stalactites, etc.

CAVE. A natural underground cavity or passage. The term is often restricted to those cavities not requiring tackle for exploration.

CAVE PEARLS. Small unattached concretions of stalactitic calcite usually formed in pools round nuclei of rock. Clusters of pearls in a pool are often called " nests."

CAVERN. Usually restricted to large chambers in caves or to large cave systems.

CHAMBER. A relatively large part of a cave.

CHERT. A cryptocrystalline form of silica found as nodules, etc., in limestones and often weathered out as projections from walls or forming pebbles on the floors of caves.

CHIMNEY. An ascending or descending shaft which is climbable by back and knee method.

CRAWL. Any passage which has to be traversed on hands and knees or lower, i.e., lying flat out. Often necessary to reverse out—a very tiring procedure.

CURTAIN. Either a rock barrier nearly to the floor of a passage necessitating crawling OR a thin elongate dripstone (stalactite) formation on walls or roof.

DEADS. Stacked boulders, usually mine debris, at the side of a passage. Often " supported " by wood of unknown age and dangerously unstable.

DOG TOOTH SPAR. A pointed form of calcite crystals.

DOLOMITE. A mineral composed of carbonate of calcium and magnesium. Or a rock chiefly composed of that mineral.

102

DRIPSTONE. A general term to cover formations deposited by dripping water, i.e. stalactites and stalagmites, etc.

DUCK. A short water-filled passage necessitating complete immersion. Usually restricted to those with a little air-space.

EFFLUENT CAVE. A cave from which water flows out.

ERRATICS. Boulders transported by ice action.

FAULT. A fracture in rocks causing relative displacement of the two sides either vertically or horizontally. Fault-surfaces are often marked by grooving known as Slickensides.

FISSURE. A natural narrow but relatively high passage, often in a joint or fault, but the term does not necessarily signify displacement.

FLOWSTONE. Stalactitic or stalagmitic formation deposited as a sheet on walls or floors, usually from a film of gently moving water.

FORMATION. Either a group of strata bearing a name OR any kind of mineral deposit in a cave, such as stalactites, gypsum, clay, etc.

GINGING. The " dry " stone walling supporting the loose ground round the top of a mine shaft. Often unstable and best avoided.

GOUR. A pool rimmed by deposited calcite, usually in association with stalagmites. Also called **RIMSTONE POOL.**

GROTTO. A cave or chamber well-decorated with stalactites.

HELICTITE. A stalactitic formation of calcite, aragonite, or gypsum, which does not grow vertically, and which may branch. Often wrongly known as Erratics.

JOINT. Natural fractures of rock strata without displacement. Often perpendicular to bedding.

KARABINER. A metal snap-link used for attachment to a rope, ladder or belay.

LEVEL. A horizontal passage in a mine, sometimes the entrance. A " Coffin level " has a cross-section like a coffin and usually dates from before explosives were introduced.

LIFELINE. A strong safety rope attached to anyone negotiating difficult obstacles or climbing ladders, etc., paid out and kept taught by a lifeliner.

LIMESTONE. A rock composed of more than 50 per cent. calcium carbonate, the remainder being sand, clay, shale, dolomite, chert, etc., etc.
Dolomitised limestone has been altered by the introduction of magnesium after deposition. Reef limestones differ in bedding and jointing characters from most other limestones, and there is some evidence in Derbyshire that they contain more caves.

MASTER-CAVE. A rather hypothetical concept of a "main drain" cave of large proportions which takes all the drainage from an area via many tributaries. Only Peak and Speedwell Caverns approach this concept in Derbyshire.

MOON-MILK. A colloidal form of calcium carbonate, believed to be deposited by bacterial action and usually found near entrances.

OX-BOW. An abandoned stream meander passage, sometimes providing a dry by-pass to a wet section.

PHREATIC. Either a cave or a feature in a cave formed by solution below the water-table.

PIPE-VEIN. A mineral vein elongated along the bedding.

PITCH. A vertical or near-vertical descent usually requiring tackle.

PITON. A metal spike or peg driven into the rock for a belay.

POT. A vertical chamber entered at the top (the same chamber could be an aven if entered from below).

POTHOLE. A vertical pitch open to the surface, or a cave system dominated by vertical descents requiring tackle. OR a hollow in a stream bed worn out by stones swirling in the water. also called a ROCK MILL.

RAKE. A large mineral vein whose workings can often be traced across country for a mile or so. Usually near vertical.

RESURGENCE. The re-appearance of an underground stream at the surface whose source is known.

RISING. The appearance of a stream on the surface whose source is unknown.

RIFT. Strictly should apply only to chambers opened by faulting but often applied to any large chamber elongated in the vertical plane.

RIMSTONE. Calcite deposited round the edge of a pool.

RUCKLE. A jumble of large boulders, sometimes large enough to be penetrated by crawling between them.

SCALLOPS. Current-marking or facetting of rock due to turbulent water flow.

SHAFT. A vertical entrance or extension to a mine, sometimes used for mine-like pots in caves.

SHACK, SHAKE or **SHAKEHOLE.** A depression in the ground surface due to the collapse of a cave beneath.

SINK or **SINKHOLE.** Any place where water disappears underground or has done so in the past.

SIPHON. A term often used incorrectly for a trap or sump, but which should strictly apply only to those with siphon action as evidenced by ebbing-and-flowing.

SLICKENSIDES. Polished, striated or grooved surface of a fault plane.

SOUGH. A mine drainage level; sometimes forms the entrance to a mine or cave.

SPELEOLOGY. The scientific study of caves.

SQUEEZE. A narrow part of a cave passable only with effort. Care about return often necessary.

STALACTITE. A cave formation, usually of calcite, hanging from the roof.

STRAW-STALACTITE. A stalactite of straw-like dimensions and hollow.

STALAGMITE. A cave formation building up from the floor, usually calcite, other forms must be specified.

STEMPLE. A wooden bar set between notches in the rock walls for miners' climbing purposes, often one of a series forming a ladder. Sometimes later used as a support for stacked deads. Usually rotten and not to be trusted.

SUMP or **TRAP.** A submerged passage, sometimes passable by diving. A sump in a mine can be any short underground shaft.

SWALLET or **SWALLOW.** Any hole taking a stream underground from the surface, OR in a mine a natural hole draining the workings.

TACKLE. Equipment needed for descending a cave or pothole, i.e., ladders, ropes, etc.

TETHER. A belay or to belay.

TRAP. A short sump which can be passed by diving.

TRAVERSE. A climb along ledges, etc., above the floor of a passage or pothole.

TUBE. A small passage of nearly circular cross-section. A roof-tube is the upper half of a tube left by downward erosion of the floor.

VADOSE. A cave or part of a cave formed by freely running water above or at the water-table.

WATER-TABLE. The surface of the zone of permanent saturation. It may fluctuate with weather and seasons. A perched water-table is held above the usual height by a local barrier to downward percolation.